STEPHEN HAWKING SMOKED MY SOCKS

Hilton Ratcliffe

Los Angeles   Santa Barbara

Stephen Hawking Smoked My Socks

A Muse Harbor Publishing Book

PUBLISHING HISTORY

Muse Harbor Publishing paperback edition
published November 2014

Published by
Muse Harbor Publishing, LLC
Los Angeles, California
Santa Barbara, California

Cover and Illustrations by Dave Workman
Interior Design by Typeflow

ISBN 978-1-61264-165-2

Visit Muse Harbor Publishing at
www.museharbor.com

*This book is dedicated to two dear
friends who have passed on:*

Sir Patrick Caldwell Moore, CBE, FRS, FRAS
(4 March 1923 – 9 December 2012)

and

Dr Halton Christian "Chip" Arp
(21 March 1927 – 28 December 2013)

CONTENTS

About Socks 'n Smoking 'n Stuff…   *vii*

Acknowledgements   *ix*

Prologue   *xi*

The Speed of Lies in a Vacuum   1

Cogito, Ergo, Sum   17

Science Is as Science Does   55

Belief, Instinct, Behaviour   94

Scepticism and Pragmatism   138

A Conspiracy of Theories   171

The Mystery of Property and Nations   219

The World According to Hawking   260

The $64,000 Question   276

Buzz Clips   298

Glossary   325

Bibliography   335

About the Author   339

I do not question Islam because I am a Christian; I do not critique Christianity because I am a Jew; I do not deny Mayan Doomsday ideas because they conflict with my belief in Nostradamus; I do not challenge Greenpeace because I am a member of the National Rifle Association; and I do not attack the 9/11 conspiracy theories because I am a Republican. In every case, I assess those belief systems using the objective scientific method, and in every case they are found wanting. And I remain in all cases an agnostic.

ABOUT SOCKS 'N SMOKING 'N STUFF...

WE NEED TO TALK. Along the way, this work attracted the whimsical working title *Socks*, so I suppose I'd better tell you why before someone gets the wrong end of the stick ...

In the global village that Carl Sagan visualised so brilliantly as the Pale Blue Dot, a dismaying trend towards androgyny in an increasingly virtual world view is still — thankfully — passionately resisted in the trenches of culturalism. The yin-yang polarities that keep this old world spinning around retain the sexiness of opposites, the challenge of antimatter, and the delight of mysterious differentness.

But — and I'm sorry to have to tell you this — there are a couple of snags. Whilst we can cope, and admirably so, with the chasm that divides the grammatical bird's nest of British English and the colloquial platitudes of American English, and even the sensible mayhem of rugby versus the regimented chaos of the NFL (to say nothing of cricket and baseball), we are not nearly so successful in embracing the idioms that isolate themselves on either side of the Atlantic Ocean. The title of this book unexpectedly highlights the problem, so I shall have to deal with it.

Smoking one's socks is a slang expression, quite common in my neck of the woods, which means coming to an opinion from a dopey state of mind. It's an artistic, tongue-in-cheek way of saying that you disagree with someone because they're nuts. It's neither malicious nor disrespectful, and does nothing to diminish the high regard in which I hold Stephen Hawking. As I know the man, he has against all odds retained his wryly subtle British sense of humour, and I fully expect in due course to have a reply from him in the best Anglo-Saxon tradition.

Until then, I have written this book to keep you amused. Be warned — it takes *no* prisoners! Read on, brave heart....

*It is difficult to free fools from
the chains they revere.*

VOLTAIRE, PHILOSOPHER AND WRITER (1694–1778)

ACKNOWLEDGEMENTS

THIS BOOK WOULD NOT be a real thing, open before you now, if it were not for the insistence, encouragement, hospitality, advice, and above all, selfless patience of Ian Campbell-Gillies. He stands out by virtue of his sheer humanity. Thank you, Ian.

Ian and I are members of a gang; the other members of our society are Eileen Workman, Cliff Saunders, Oliver Manuel, and Denis Beckett. I tortured them continuously over the two years it took me to bring this book to fruition, and it was their stoicism and unstinting moral support that carried me this far. My companions, I thank you.

The proprietors of Muse Harbor Publishing, Eileen and Dave Workman, have been absolutely wonderful. Their humanity and empathy — to say nothing of their incisive intellect and wise-owl eyes — reached out over cyberspace to bridge the ocean between San Francisco and Durban. What a pleasure it is to do business like this, especially in a world of publishing badged by the bones of crushed authors and shattered dreams. Making a living by selling books is more difficult now than it ever was, and that's as true for publishers as it is for authors. Thank you, my friends.

I wish at this juncture to take my hat in my hand and pay homage to the giants upon whose shoulders I stood, and who have since passed from the Earthly realm. They are Professor Tony Bray, Dr Halton "Chip" Arp, Professor Geoffrey Burbidge, Sir Patrick Moore, Dr Tom Van Flander, Sir Bernard Lovell, Dr Hannes Alfvén, and Sir Fred Hoyle. How on Earth I managed to outlive them all, I shall never know. My solemn hope is that I do their memory proud. Sirs, you knew before you passed that one day I would publicly thank you for your guidance and support. Though it is pathetically inadequate, here I say it: thank you.

In conclusion of these meagre acknowledgements, I should also like to thank an unlikely hero. Thank you, Dr Stephen Hawking.

Hilton Ratcliffe
Durban, South Africa
February, 2014

PROLOGUE

IN EARLY JANUARY 2014, just days after I had submitted what I thought to be the final, final, final draft of this book to my publishers for editing, Stephen Hawking dropped a bombshell. He published a paper in the esteemed journal *Nature*, in which he cautiously alluded to something of absolutely dazzling importance, both to the world of science and to this book. In a few, almost conversational pages with no mathematics at all, Dr Hawking turned his world and mine on their heads. I had to urgently recall the manuscript and make some hastily written changes to bring my text into line with an entirely unexpected, heroic vindication from no less than the man himself. A gift from the gods, one might be tempted to say.

Dr Hawking had finally given expression to what must have been a nagging doubt that had troubled him for decades. Do black holes actually exist? Let us not concern ourselves with what black holes are in the minds of cosmologists and theoretical physicists. Suffice it to say that black holes are theoretical constructs — monstrous objects presumed by some to exist in deep space — that possibly and ominously portend our extinction as a species and portray the eventual, inevitable doom of the entire universe. It is upon this vision of metaphysical hypercreatures that the youthful Stephen Hawking based his academic research, and upon which he constructed his illustrious career over a period spanning half a century. And which he, in January 2014, finally admitted might not be real after all.

It is profoundly important that I state up front what this book is about: the power and influence of belief over data-driven science in creating our opinions, and the eternal, polarising conflict between belief and instinct in the development of our mindset. This book is not about my scientific theories, nor does it promote my personal models of the universe. Please bear in mind that I am not proposing an alternative model of anything; I am merely tendering a method that favours objectivity in the development of all theories and philosophies, whatever they might be. I state my motives quite explicitly at several places in the book, and in the final chapter say this:

"I am a believer as much as anyone, and my world view is undoubtedly coloured by my own prejudice. What I am going to suggest in this concluding chapter is a systematic approach by which we can more closely align our stubborn mindset with objective truth. I'm not offering an alternative model. I'm not selling an explanation of the universe. What I'm asking everyone, especially my brethren in science, is to urgently review the *method* they employ. If we can but reduce the contamination inherent in method, we will automatically and without further ado be more clearly exposed to objective truth. We need to wipe some mud off the foundations before we build our castles of light."[1]

Nowhere in *Socks* do I state that in my opinion black holes do not exist. What I believe about the universe is irrelevant to the arguments in *Socks*. We need to put Stephen Hawking's latest declarations into that context. His entire career, and all his research, was based upon his *a priori* conviction that black holes are real objects that physically exist in nature. My contention is that Hawking's model was obtained from subjective opinions that directed the way he solved equations, and most certainly not from analysing empirical data. What Hawking has done at the twilight of his career is finally admit a healthy scepticism of his most dearly held conviction. It's analogous to Edwin Hubble casting doubt on cosmological redshift (which he did in his book, papers, and lectures), and Peter Woit publishing *Not Even Wrong*, which retracted everything he'd ever said as one of string theory's leading gurus.

The intellectual and ethical integrity demanded by such actions is so rare that it occurs in the lives of usually just two or three opinion makers in each century, and Dr Stephen Hawking has shown by this that he is one of them.

---

1 Chapter 9, "The $64,000 Question".

The staggering importance of his recent pronouncement is not in any way connected to his agreeing or disagreeing with my personal cosmology (not that I would ever have such a thing) but that he has demonstrated the moral strength to shake off the very belief upon which he built his entire working life in science. It's akin to the Pope denying Catholic Christianity.

I must be clear from the word *go*: This examination of the power of belief in human nature is driven by my experiences in astrophysics over several decades. Given my background and training in classical celestial mechanics and chemistry, it was no wonder that I would before long become thoroughly disillusioned with the theoretical end of my field. I simply could not understand why there was such an intense and dogmatic insistence upon the prior conversion of undergraduate physicists to what was after all just a philosophical model. The way we were to practice our craft was to a large extent determined and constrained by the compulsory assumption of a particular philosophical world view. It was the Big Bang way or the highway. Full conversion to the faith was the only realistic path to a degree in space science.

This I found repugnant. With my tail bushed out and my ears flattened, I began a campaign of resistance that was to last forty years. The defining moment in my quest for enlightenment in this frustrating maelstrom came in conversation with the late Professor Geoffrey Burbidge. "Hilton," he said to me a few months before he died, "the problem is really this: The administrators of education in space science will be extremely loath to abandon the Big Bang theory, because if they do it will amount to an explicit admission that they actually know far less than they have led us all to believe. That's the problem. Their pride will simply not allow it."

Well, that was it. I was determined to get to the bottom of this iniquitous state of affairs, even if that meant taking a diversion from hard physics and immersing myself in the heady, turbulent, often opaque ocean of the humanities. I must say, I'm so glad I did. The ultimate result of my detour is this book, a presentation of my thesis on the sociological, political, and behavioural roots of opinions, convictions, dogma, and bias in physical science. The phenomenon is pervasive, and affects everyone who has an opinion, so my quest has been generalised to take in a broad range of scientific and sociopolitical disciplines. I contend that everyone, without exception, is powerfully affected by personal belief, so I suppose I have at last produced a book that is relevant to seven billion people.

The aim of this discourse is not to prove one of us right and the other wrong, but for us both to find an accurate and realistic way of looking at the world. No hocus-pocus. There's a tree in my garden, and I can see it through my study window. It's about fifteen metres away, and it has mauve blossoms. I have been to that tree, touched it, smelt it, studied it, photographed it, and learnt from it. Do I believe it is really there? Yes I do. Do I believe that if I were to drop down dead this instant, the tree would still be there, blossoming and being visited by birds? Yes I do. Am I sure about that? I'm certain. I have no doubt whatsoever.

So this tree forms part of my personal dogma. It would be counterproductive to my quest for real knowledge to entertain lengthy exchanges of arguments on whether or not that tree is real. From my point of view, it would be useless also to defend my opinion that notwithstanding the mumbled assertions of some vaguely conscious hippies of my acquaintance, this tree does not by some surreptitious means conceal the lair of the Easter Bunny. My mother-in-law believes in fairies. Really, really believes in fairies. I do not. We both know that fairies are not something we should be discussing. I love visiting her, and we sit and have tea and laugh and remember and talk about stuff. Just not about fairies. Life's too short to squabble about fairies, really....

Why did Stephen Hawking become so famous? What is it exactly that brought world renown to Albert Einstein? There must be a good reason why those are household names across the globe, why their faces are icons rivalling those of film stars, and why they are adored and protected by a fierce fan club. The realisation hit me like a splash of cold water — *it has nothing at all to do with science.* If it did, then we would display their wares on our coffee tables shoulder to shoulder with photographic tributes to Christiaan Barnard, Francis Crick, and Kristian Birkeland. *Who*, you ask? Exactly.

I owe my late father a huge debt of gratitude for impressing upon me the value of what I would in later years call *reality physics*. He spoke to me about physics and mechanics, cause and effect, from the time I was first able to hold memories in my mind's eye. The way he put this philosophy to me seemed so simple that it appeared to be patently naive, yet it would take me until well into my adult years before I ultimately grasped the meaning of these idioms.

- No hocus-pocus.
- Beware the man with a theory.
- Never negotiate with a suicide bomber.
- For every effect, there's a cause, and for every action, a reaction.

Whatever the truth of the matter, and no matter our belief system, we are all children of the universe, given to contemplation and abstract thought. Let's take that levelling notion along with us as we explore the sanctity of belief. Hopefully, we'll come out the other side of this book less confused than when we went in.

If you must play, decide on three things
at the start: the rules of the game, the
stakes, and the quitting time.

CHINESE PROVERB

We strut our stuff amongst the biological diversity of our lonely blue planet as it speeds towards an unseen destiny, proclaiming ourselves advanced merely because we have the faculty of abstract thought; the singular privilege of being able to think about thought, to juggle between the senses and a self-centred theory of mind, and to furiously engage in sharing our imaginations with anyone who dares to listen.

1

THE SPEED OF LIES
IN A VACUUM

What's wrong with the world?

THE FINAL CONFLICT FOR spaceship Earth: the battle between instinct and belief. It's a savage war that shreds our coherence as a global tribe, and sets us apart from creatures without the agency of belief. Homo sapiens carry with themselves an exaggerated sense of self. It is the inevitable consequence, it would seem, of our hard-wired capacity for noble thought. We strut our stuff amongst the biological diversity of our lonely blue planet as it speeds towards an unseen destiny, proclaiming ourselves advanced merely because we have the faculty of abstract thought — the singular privilege of being able to think *about* thought, to toggle between the senses and a self-centred theory of mind, and to furiously engage in sharing our imaginations with anyone who dares to listen.

Disagreeing with instinct appears to be a dichotomy peculiar to the human species; other animals, though as capable as we are of making choices in the moment, are not (as far as I can tell) perplexed and misled by such an elaborate belief in the sanctity of their own opinions. The purity of subhuman behaviour is a beacon in the cosmos, providing an indispensible parameter for scientists longing for objective truth. Everything I stand for, and all that I have written, is indelibly contaminated by my own belief. It is inescapable. Human beings are designed to believe, and not even the most irrational drooling idiot is exempt from having dogmatic opinions. It is my contention that when faced with such disturbances of the psyche, our most sensible course of action is to accept and abide.

Unfortunately, there is no way I can break this to you gently. In South Africa we recently experienced a reverberating tragedy as a direct consequence of ill-found belief. It has become known in the annals of our tormented country as the Marikana massacre. Militant strikers at a platinum mine in the area, armed with a variety of weapons, advanced threateningly on a cordon of police officers. Tension ran high; the strikers had already openly and gruesomely killed at least ten people, including policemen, security guards, and union officials, and mutilated their bodies with clear intent. The strikers chanted and flaunted battle rituals that echoed the style of Zulu *impis*[1] from a bygone, martial era. They came down the hillside at a steady canter, and closed without fear on the ranks of machine-gun-toting police. Their brazen advance ignited the powder keg that had for weeks threatened fragile

---

1 Impi: Zulu word meaning military regiment.

attempts at negotiated peace. When it blew, a whole new generation of widows and orphans was born at Marikana. In less than ten seconds, the death-rattle of 5.56mm hard-point bullets laid thirty-four of the charging throng so low they would rise no more. The dust settled, the blood dried on the parched Highveld grass, and the political posturing and blame game began.

News video holds a stark record of much of the action during those crucial, angry days, so we gained an unusually detailed insight into what went down at Marikana. We saw the sickening detail of those horrifying images on television: hacked and ritually mutilated bodies that stared straight at our collective conscience with gruesome eyeless sockets. It will take sociologists years to sift through the information to find out how it fits with known patterns of human behaviour, but already we can deduce a great deal. One thing the video footage clearly reveals is the ceremonial application of *muti*[2] to the protesting miners by local sangomas[3], and anyone who knows anything about traditional African tribal practice would be in no doubt whatsoever what that meant. The miners were preparing for battle.

The muti is intended to make those using it impervious to their enemies' weapons; in this case, muti transformed

---

2 Muti: From the Zulu word for tree, the more benign meaning of muti is herbal remedy; an altogether more sinister meaning comes with its application to traditional tribal occult practices, where it is claimed to have supernatural power.

3 Sangoma: A diviner; master of the occult; a priest in tribal ancestral worship. Not to be confused with nyanga, a traditional healer and herbalist.

the miners into bulletproof super warriors who could not be stopped or turned aside. They appeared not to have a moment's doubt, and with their pangas and spears and knobkieries, they were resolute. The miners on that koppie were brazenly fearless.

And into the valley of Death rode the six hundred.

Of course it didn't work. The muti has no material effect other than a smell somewhat like a neglected latrine. Two things in particular interest us here: Firstly that those strikers so believed in the genuine supernatural ability of sangomas that they literally staked their lives on it; and secondly, despite an entirely predictable outcome based on the one hundred percent failure rate of all previous attempts to get the voodoo to work — and notwithstanding the vivid demonstration of sangomas' fraud at Marikana — there remain survivors who believe it still. No doubt they attribute their escape to the charming qualities of paranormal potions rather than the fact that they had somewhat fortuitously stayed clear of the line of fire. Even in defeat, their faith was reinforced. We have witnessed a profound and tragic demonstration of the stupefying power of belief.

The world is a mess. As far as I can tell, it always has been. Let me qualify that: The lack of coherence is a human perception, so it's more accurate to say that the world has been a mess for as long as we've been around. The Hindu epic *Bhagavad Gita* tells in allegory of an almighty struggle between good and evil, where the divine warrior Arjuna takes his sword to the dark forces stalking humankind's better judgement. Today, the same battle rages on, always between polar extremes, but I have assigned the archangels better names.

I too perceive humanity's self-defeating efforts at raising itself to a podium of glory amongst creatures of the commonwealth as a conflict between forces dark and light; but there is no need to camouflage those forces with heavenly heroes and satanic villains. We know the protagonists in this particular war extremely well. The human condition, for better or for worse, is the residue of a deadly struggle, and that struggle is between free will and the primordial code that constrains our species, between *belief* and *instinct*.

Uncovering the historical roots of belief systems is a hazardous affair. If truth be told, uncovering the roots of *anything* is a hazardous affair, and in the biography of man, especially fraught with fractures and voids. What real wisdom existed before the age of information technology? Admittedly, all I and other scholars have to go on is a collection of legends, ancient oral traditions, and cave paintings distilled to crude symbolic letters and plastered mystifyingly onto the dusty walls of antiquity. Anthropologists and fortune hunters and imperial armies (sometimes the distinction is maddeningly blurred) toiled under foreign skies to plunder the Rosetta stones that might have made things clearer, had they only been stolen by more scholarly hands. Nevertheless, we should be devoutly appreciative of those who looted by royal decree, for it was they who plucked the lost letters from the sands of time and brought them back to try to divine some pertinent meaning in the message. This is the great frustration of deciphering history by means of archaeology and anthropology — what on Earth were those dim and distant ancestors trying to tell us? What were they thinking? We can never be sure....

The invention of paper brought about a methodological revolution in the recording of history. No longer would we have to depend upon flaking murals and chipped and broken clay tablets presenting stick figures and squiggles and heads with funny hats. Combined with the invention of phonetic alphabets and mathematical language, paper opened a gaping portal to a new and wonderful world, an altered landscape where Today can pass on its ideas in polymorphous detail to the unseen, unborn audience of Tomorrow.

The first books were scrolls, and the first scribes, priests. It didn't take long for the masters of manipulation to realise that the currency of war included the parchments and libraries of thinking men. It occurred to the pharaohs that if you slaughter the ideas, you cow the nation, and that has been a principle of militant politics ever since.

Sadly, paper burns more easily than do pyramids. Even in this age of electronic, virtual paper, the fire burns on. The swords wielded in battle today are cyber blades; weapons have kept pace with the technology that put words into the sky for us all to read. Rogues and despots are so much easier to breed these days; all you need is a smartphone and an Internet connection, and you can go to war.

Using the principle of antimatter, of a vacuum swallowing pressure, the messengers of doom divert the goodness of truth with conspiracy theories. It's a sly craft that they preach. They trade upon the certainty that the human animal is a Pavlovian slave, and the unslaked dust in our mental desert is just the place to pour toxic constructs and cultivate the obsession. It's a sinister game where the power has shifted towards the proletariat — no longer is the grail of empire held exclusively and unilaterally by Napoleon or Bush or Chairman Mao. You and I can do it too, but by all that's holy, what an almighty mess we are making of the privilege. The unleashing onto the global information game of naively self-serving, faith-blinkered intellectual paupers and egotistical, money-grabbing idea warriors, has given baby a box of matches.

Some of those ancient scribes with rolls of papyrus and sheepskin parchment must have sensed that their books posed a threat to the ravenous oligarchy. They took what they could and hid them before the swords of imperial wrath could fall. In clay pots in Dead Sea caves all over the literate world, the scholars of written words concealed their wisdom. They did it so well that most are lost forever. But thank heavens they did make an effort, because the war on knowledge took no prisoners, and it is upon those surviving scraps that we feed for truth. We cannot rely on politically correct, factually sanitised official versions of history; I heard it said, by someone who would know, that the Vatican would never dare to put its archives into the public domain, for if they did, the Church would crumble and fall. It makes one wonder, doesn't it, why the Roman Catholic Church wants to keep those things such a closely guarded secret. What is it exactly that they so earnestly hide in a dusty box under the papal bed, and why?

In 48 BC, Caesar's troops sacked the Egyptian delta and razed the great library of Alexandria to the ground. The fire destroyed the original scripts of Aeschylus, Sophocles, and Euripides, along with uncounted texts of the Ptolemaic era. Later, in AD 325 when the emperor Constantine ordered the Council of Nicea to put some political direction into ragtag Christian ideology, literature bent profoundly to that wind. Constantine charged the notorious Bishop Eusebius with the task of censorship, and under Eusebius's draconian hand perished — forever — untold volumes of written witness to the advent of the Christian ideology. The reason? Simply because they didn't align with Constantine's political ambitions.

Great science, dominant philosophies, and conquests of religion have taken themselves to dizzying heights of self-adulation and zeal, and they have all, every single one of them, been based upon a small (dare I say even trivial?) portion of prior wisdom that survived the ravages of time and bloody-minded politics. Promising thoughts and collective insights are diverted by crazy ideas, cleverly put. So much of what we believe is what someone with sinister intent *wants* us to believe, and they are damned good at making their case. It's tragic.

Nevertheless, we have to make do with what we have. Thanks to the dissidents of the time, we do have that small representation of historical witness that they managed to save. We have to take whatever they wrote down at face value, bearing in mind that the farther away something is, in space or in time, the greater is our uncertainty. Our need for circumspection is thus all the more pressing. The details are vague and open to a cartload of interpretive variation, but at least this much is clear: It's a long, sorry tale.

A few years back while on a visit to the late astronomer and truth warrior Sir Patrick Moore at his home in West Sussex, I took a drive to the gracefully historic city of Bath. My purpose was to experience the museum honouring legendary astronomer-musician Sir William Herschel, and also to see something of the city that has seduced visitors for centuries. From the moment I wove my car into the tangled streets, I was awestruck. What enchanting, sweeping beauty! The curved terrace houses on the hillside overlooking the town centre are majestic, forming a magnificent backdrop to the abbey, the river, the famous bridge, and the weir. I met my host for the day, a professor at the university there, at his apartment in one of those terraces about a mile from the downtown area. I parked my car and we spent the day on foot.

It was a cold, rainy December morning, but I didn't care. I felt I was connecting to history, feeling ghosts that I couldn't quite see, sensing whispered words I could hardly hear. We wandered along streets that must have looked just as they did when William Herschel and Charles Dickens lived here over a century ago. Rain dressed the flagstones in delicate, mystic sheens, striking sombre harmonies with the browns and greys of gloriously geometric terraces. There were no vivid colours, no neon, no garish hoardings to break the spell; I could feel, touch, smell the world almost exactly as Herschel and Dickens and Jane Austen had. I felt inspired by it, as they had been. But there was always a tantalising question hovering in the back of my mind as we walked along, the good professor and I, both limping from prior wounds but oblivious to the pain: Where would this ripple in time and space take me?

We took our morning tea at the Roman baths, treated to crisp white linen and silver spoons in a wonderfully Dickensian lounge called the Pump House. A dark-suited ensemble performed on violin and cello the same Herschel chamber music on the very same tiny stage that, in an age gone by, the gifted astronomer himself had used to entertain passing strangers such as I. I was enthralled, caught in the moment, lost on a cloud of romance and mystery and shadowy fleeting figures in topcoats and powdered wigs. We talked and talked, and sipped our tea, and absorbed the atmosphere until that scene was done. We stepped out once again onto the preordained rainy sidewalk, making our way along pedestrian streets to the town square and, finally, into the aura of the hauntingly beautiful Bath Abbey. It stood resolutely in the drizzle and cold, unblinking in all its gothic glory after more than a thousand years guarding the holy tradition of kings. There is no way I could ever have foreseen how deeply meaningful that visit to a church would turn out to be. It was to become a milestone on my journey.

Now, I'm not the sort of chap who readily patronises churches. I suppose, by comparison with the believing flock, I run my life at some considerable spiritual deficit, but it has never been clear to me how I could turn that to profit by partaking in the programme offered by churches. They are places of great mystery to me, so much so that I've tended to avoid them whenever I had the choice. I must admit, though, that there is also something about churches that impresses me, particularly the old ones that were designed and built with tangible reverence. The classical architecture proclaims an immense history, filled with passion and pathos, intrigue and drama, and yes, I suppose on the odd occasion, also a touch of joy and even sporadic communication with God Almighty. Mostly, it is drama on a high stage, with all the accoutrements of theatre; the costumes, the sets, the music, and the heroic speeches, all pay tribute to a playwright-director hiding somewhere in the wings.

I stood in the squalling rain next to a sodden busking guitarist with an empty hat, soaking up the ambience of the towering west front. Photographs cannot do it justice — a golden arch of warm Bath stone with its single immense slatted window, flanked on either side by stone ladders upon which delicately carved angels hung frozen in their ascent to the heavens — and suddenly my heresy plagued me. It was as if that severe, stony facade had eyes behind the mask, and they were glaring right at me. I couldn't help feeling that I was looking at a picture of God wearing Ray-Bans. From time to time I embarrass myself with thoughts like this.

We passed through a smaller door to the left of the grand entrance. I was surprised and somewhat flattered to be greeted there by the vicar, in his official dress, at half past eleven on a Tuesday morning. The professor told me that the abbey was after all this time still a working church where he enjoyed taking sacrament of a Sunday, and that the vicar was a deeply learned man with a brace of doctorates. I'm such a schmuck, I didn't know whether that meant I had to salute him in a special way or perhaps curtsey, but I've learnt one thing over the years — being overtly South African means I can get clean away with all manner of rustic ineptitudes.

Inside, the abbey is nothing short of breathtaking, but in a very unusual way. It's not all that big in the league of cathedrals, nor is it brashly decorated with partisan signals of providence. It's just *old*, in the most alluring way. My host did his best to get me to relax, but I was just too stoned on the atmosphere. He pointed out the plaques on the walls marking the interred earthly remains of a millennium's worth of parishioners who were able to afford such singular privilege; engraved flags in the floor where deeds most foul had stained the sanctity of faith in Norman England; and the pews of English oak that had distinct, bum-shaped hollows sculpted by the abrasive tweed behinds of centuries of devout worshippers.

I looked up and gasped; seventy five feet overhead was the most magnificent fan-vaulted stone ceiling, and in an alcove on the northern side, an organ so majestic, I believed it would make the gods themselves weep. And all of this noble, monastic severity was bathed in the rainbow light of vast stained glass windows. Diffuse cloudy sunlight filtered through the lead-light frames of saints and angels and lit up a beaming tragic messiah.

Was I impressed? Gosh yes. More than that, I was inspired. I felt small, but at the same time, wantonly enriched. I was standing in the bosom of a fantastic monument, about to gain fragile purchase on the threshold of understanding. What is it all about?

Dear reader, I shall keep you in suspense no longer; there *was* something important that happened to me in the Bath Abbey, and it concerns the induction of a king. One of the engraved stone tiles inside the church describes the coronation of Edgar, the first king of England. That was fascinating enough, but what really hit me between the eyes was who had performed the service of crowning the king. The service was devised and administered by Dunstan, the archbishop of Canterbury, more than a thousand years ago, and it forms the basis of British coronation ceremonies right up to the present day. It took some time for the essential point to sink in — standing there in the shadowy heart of the Bath Abbey, it slowly dawned on me that there had been an archbishop of Canterbury before there ever was a King of all England. There was a Church of England long before there was an England.

This led to a whole new, astonishing train of thought. The system of government by means of an absolute monarchy, installed by order of birth and protected by the so-called divine right of kings, is possibly one of the worst ideas ever devised in the way that we organise ourselves as nations, rivalling communism in the league of political nightmares. Kings and queens installed to absolute power like this are bound to be miserable clots at best, and raving, despotic lunatics at worst. There is no test in either the public domain or in secret to ensure the suitability of the next in line to lead a nation. Nothing more than the privilege of their often capricious parentage allowed anyone, of whatever mental capacity, to hold in their sweaty royal palms the fate and fortunes of all who lived in the realm. The wanton excess of those who fortuitously found themselves in sole possession of the whole cookie jar led to offspring of dubious lineage, plagued by the diseases of nobility, and these spoilt brats duly became kings and queens.

It is indeed the power that corrupts. Witness the graciousness with which Elizabeth the Second occupies the present day monarchy. The contrast is stark: relieved of the power over life and death, she is free to be magnificent.

Edgar was barely sixteen years old when he became king of Wessex upon the death of his elder brother Edwy in AD

959, and only thirty when he declared himself supreme lord of all the mini-kingdoms of England put together. Within two years of ascending to the throne, he was dead, just thirty-two years of age. His demise, we learn from chronicles of the day, was not attributable to wholesome living.

It was some years after my trip to Bath that I found further implications of this system of rule. You see, it extends to ideas and beliefs as well. Ideas, in the form of theories, are treated like the favourite courtiers of a king; they are canonised and ultimately raised to sainthood. The so-called standard models have no effective opposition; the next model to take over will be the progeny of the incumbent. The lineage is strictly enforced, and the curricula of higher learning are unwaveringly obedient to the divine right of belief. You cannot, at any university I've ever heard of, take a degree in astrophysics without swearing allegiance to the Big Bang theory, or read in biology free of the constraint of Darwinian evolution, or try to get a qualification in the field of gravitation unless you promise to stick strictly to the general relativity theory. I am not suggesting that any or all of these theories are completely wrong. They may well be, but that's not the point. The issue at play in academia, as in life in general, is that these are just theories, ideas held passionately by those that rule, nothing more. There are indeed obvious elements of truth in all standard models — how else could they have become standard models? — but there should be no sacred cows. It is one thing to believe; quite another to declare one's belief unquestionably infallible, and defend it at all costs.

The kings of knowledge are all-powerful in the realm they administer, and it has surely corrupted them. Like despots anywhere, they should (figuratively speaking, of course) be put to the sword, and let the next king ascend to start the whole caboodle all over again. Let the scribes of history bear witness: We have new messiahs, no less tragic than the martyred, self-immolated heroes of theological legend, and their influence is profound. From the turgid shadows of the nuclear age and the era of covert global warfare arose a man who came to symbolise everything good and everything bad about our forlorn quest for true knowledge. Imprisoned by a twisted, broken body, and communicating by nothing more than the movement of his eyes, Dr Stephen Hawking has only his mind left to offer.

In our compassion and our wonder, we have taken that remote imagination as holy sacrament, and now we must pay the price.

Convictions are more dangerous enemies of truth than lies.

FRIEDRICH WILHELM NIETZSCHE,
PHILOSOPHER (1844–1900)

If we hold the opinion that the Sun is the nucleus of the Solar System because we interpret a passage in the Bible that way, it is belief; if, on the other hand, we maintain the very same opinion as a result of geometrical measurement and observation, it is knowledge. If we accept and embrace the validity of General Relativity Theory simply because we think Albert Einstein is awesome, we express belief; if our support of the model comes from stringent empirical testing, it is knowledge.

2

COGITO, ERGO, SUM

My world view

PULL UP A CHAIR. Make yourself comfortable. It's time to chat. It may not be readily apparent, but what I am about to propose is, to put it mildly, a departure from the norm. The human social condition is in serious disrepair, and science — where we ought to be garnering objective wisdom upon which to build the global tribe but are not — has fallen with it. Communism was chewed, tasted, and spat out by human nature; capitalism suffocates on the personal greed that fuels it; and we've bastardised democracy so severely that it is scarcely recognisable these days. Society is an unhappy place.

Viable remedies exist for our ills, but in order to consider my proposal we are going to have to suspend, temporarily at least, our most precious and jealously guarded of possessions — our beliefs. We love belief more than life itself, and what I ask may sadly be a bridge too far. I shall try to make the tribulations that follow as gentle as I possibly can. One thing I wish to make perfectly clear at the outset — I am not proposing yet another social model for Homo sapiens. We need to develop a method (which I have labelled *scientific pragmatism*) that provides us objective strata upon which to build our models. What we make of our world after that is up to us, guided by our life skills and our morality. Let's get on with it then....

The dilemma I face is both real and vexing. The sorry fact is that we don't really want to hear the truth. We just want to hear stuff that doesn't disturb our comfort zones. That poses a huge challenge from a marketing point of view: Because this book exposes the harsh reality of belief — everyone's belief — it paints itself into a corner. How many people will want to buy a book that says that no one has the right answer, even the author himself? Why should anyone pay me any attention? My answer is simply this: If we have a clear conception of what is wrong, we can try to avoid it. Even if we do not have the right answer, we can approach the truth more readily if we avoid the camouflaged traps of unreason. Upon that flimsy thread I hang my thesis. So read on, brave heart, there's a light at the end of our tunnel, and no, it's not an oncoming express train.

Please allow me to quote from *The Virtue of Heresy*[1]:

> The universe is infinite in extent, and it lasts forever. If you doubt that, ask yourself what lies beyond any arbitrary final boundary you care to imagine. Let's think it through. If the universe had a beginning, then

---

1 Hilton Ratcliffe, *The Virtue of Heresy: Confessions of a Dissident Astronomer* (CreateSpace, 2008).

what lay before it? If the answer is '*nothing*', then where did '*something*' come from? And if the answer is '*something*', then it clearly wasn't the beginning. If the universe is finite spatially, what lies beyond that horizon? Nothing? Do you *really* suggest we could travel x kilometres in any direction and come to an end of everything, including space? I don't think so. The notion of an infinite universe (in time and space) is not the result of empirical observation; it is a logical assumption. We see a universe continuing before us, and we can find no edge to it. We therefore conclude that the universe is apparently endless. To assume an end to things is as baseless as assuming that there is any other kind of critical but wholly unobserved change to what is normally the case, and in the absence of any detectable trend towards termination, we are unable even to predict such a thing. We have no reason to assume a spatial and temporal limit to the universe other than to accommodate a preferred theoretical model. If we predict a finite universe (even the finite-but-unbounded version we will discuss later on), then we should take up the challenge of finding observational evidence to support the idea. None has been found. *There is no Final Frontier.*

The first thing I ought to mention here is my approach to infinity. We cannot conceptualise infinity. Our minds can cope only with finite objects, and not very well at that. Infinity is neither a quantity nor a place. It is a parameter of existence, and in the framework of cosmology, it is entirely optional. Infinity as it applies to the spatial extent of the universe is simply endlessness. In terms of the time dimension, it implies endlessness in both directions — an infinite cosmos had no beginning and it will have no end. Although the notion of an infinite universe is for me no more than an assumption — an axiom of my world view, and therefore an article of my belief paradigm — I make mention of it for good reason.

Let me make it abundantly clear at the outset that the assumption of an infinite existence has no direct bearing on the arguments of this work. Indirectly though, it is invaluable. We shall soon be discussing the ins and outs of the empirical scientific method, and discussion of infinity is relevant in that context. There can be no empirical evidence for infinity, in whatever shape or form. Infinity is far beyond the grasp of the scientific method. It is simply belief that comes from speculation and meditation upon the deeper implications of existence.

I accept the endlessness of the cosmos because it makes sense. Applying logic to the question of the extent of the universe leaves me no option but to impute that it has no final, limiting boundary condition. Crucially, I must admit that I want the universe to be endless. The notion pleases me. So I make it an assumption upon which I build my personal philosophy. The important point being realised here is that I cannot *know* infinity. Anything I build upon that assumption has a significant degree of uncertainty. Consequently, I ought to be circumspect in my efforts to sell the idea.

Let me present just one example of what I mean. Rupert Sheldrake is a biologist and a person I admire greatly, despite his inclination away from hard science and towards parapsychology. He and I have a lot in common, and his book *Science Set Free* remains a permanent fixture on my night stand. Dr Sheldrake proposes an infinite connection called the morphic field, which he asserts (from the example of biological cells), connects all things in the entire universe. I find the notion appealing, but I see no hard evidence for it. Sheldrake *wants* there to be morphic resonance, and that to some extent blinds him to the idea's shortcomings.

Sitting beside the ocean with a good friend last weekend, I chatted and listened and drank tea and rescued the world. (Again!) As always, my friend's perspective hardened my resolve and gave me a fresh sense of purpose. It became increasingly obvious that what I'm asking my readers to do is not trivial, and that my success in this endeavour is going to rest almost entirely upon my ability to move people out of their comfort zones without unwarranted stress. I'm hoping that a sense of liberation will reward you latter-day Argonauts enough to encourage you to finish the book. It's a journey of exploration for all of us, myself included.

I have for some time now been on the cusp of expressing *the* fundamental principle of my world view. It would be something along these lines:

Most of us are "seekers", drawn towards some inner expression of the vast mysteries of existence. Seekers are divided into two main tribes — realists and dreamers — so it follows that there are two approaches to achieving understanding of the world.

First approach — the realists: realists analyse bits and pieces in our observable environment, and then add them together by category to build up a library of knowledge that can never be complete. This is the path followed by empirical science. It involves observation and experiment, constrained by the independent and immutable laws of nature. It leads by combining established fundamentals with theories of discrete parts of nature only, never with everything. It reaches no philosophical outcome except by reverting to the second approach. It is an external process. It is objective. It is epistemology. *It offers understanding*.

Second approach — the dreamers: dreamers pursue an intellectual analysis of the intellect itself. This is the path followed by philosophy. It involves imagination, superstition, and thought experiments, unconstrained by reality. It achieves no practical outcome except by reverting to the first approach. It is an internal process. It is subjective. It is ontology. *It offers meaning*.

Both methodologies have their place, but in practice they are mutually exclusive. They should be studied in separate classrooms. No doubt that each can contribute to the other, with mutual benefit, but the processes are the equivalent of oil and water. They can lie comfortably next to each other, but they don't mix.

I stress that both methodologies are relevant and effective in building the picture of the world we'll carry with us. The first gives understanding; the second, meaning. To my mind, that nails down the sequence in which we should apply these methodologies to the problems we seek to solve. First, gain understanding; then, and only then, impute meaning. The unfortunate reality is that most people do it the other way around, but then again, that's what gives this book its *raison d'être*.

Deriving opinions from intuition, imagination, and faith-based visceral revelations is immediately subjective;

our personality, that cloying expression of our deeper psyche, vests generous dollops of emotional reinforcement in our opinions, and we defend them quite irrationally at times. Scientific pragmatism rests upon the fundamental axiom that truth belongs to none of us; it is gloriously independent of our hopes and dreams, and remains pristine and unsullied by research grants and bibles. What we believe has no bearing. Perhaps that elusive principle I seek to express is this: We need to separate ego and science.

Because physicists have abandoned the empirical scientific method, they have cast themselves adrift from reality, the only safe anchorage there is for ideas. Intuitive, subjective imagining can be beautiful and often very interesting, but as a method for determining truth, it is hopeless. The vast, irreconcilable differences between religions demonstrate explicitly that faith untested against reality remains just that — faith, without any clear relevance to what is actually happening in the world about us. Any idea we come up with must be subjected to rigorous, unbiased, unemotional testing before it becomes useful in the real world. Until then, it remains just someone's musing, but — and this is the important bit — packaged cleverly enough, it can sell a mint.

There is no need to complicate the nature of truth. It is objective, and describes reality as closely as possible to its pristine state, as if there were an absence of any observer. Truth is not an opinion. Whatever the truth is, it will be the same for all of us. Science is a method for systematically uncovering the truth, not a final conclusion about the universe. What I'm seeking is the best way to establish the truth of the matter. The question the sensible seeker asks is concerned with method. How do I best approach that one truth? The optimum method, ideally, would return the same answer always, no matter who asked the question.

If we confine ourselves to the choices I have outlined above — although I am not so foolish or self-satisfied to suggest that these are our only options — then we must weigh them with this logical filter: Which of the two offers the better chance of producing the same answer for all seekers? To me, it seems obvious.

What is my purpose in creating this book? I am indebted to Michael Shermer, who might well have been writing about *Socks* when he introduced his seminal work, *The Believing Brain:* [2]

> This book synthesises thirty years of research to answer the question of how and why we believe what we do in all aspects of our lives. Here I am interested in more than just why people believe weird things, or why people believe this or that claim, but why people believe anything at all. Why do people believe? My answer is straightforward:
>
> We form our beliefs for a variety of subjective, personal, emotional, and psychological reasons in the context of environments created by family, colleagues, culture, and society at large; after forming our beliefs we then defend, justify, and rationalize them with a host of intellectual reasons, cogent arguments, and rational explanations. Beliefs come

---

2 Michael Shermer, *The Believing Brain* (New York: Times Books, 2011).

first, explanations for beliefs follow. I call this process belief-dependent realism, where our perceptions about reality are dependent on the beliefs we hold about it. Reality exists independent of the human mind, but our understanding of it depends upon the beliefs we hold at any given time.

The intent of this chapter is to introduce myself to you over a figurative cup of tea, and reveal my own philosophical mindset. It's called my point of view. As a child, I demonstrated a natural and advanced ability to solve the problems posed by mathematics. Algebra and theorems came as easily to me as whistling. I take no credit for that; I was born with it, a talent that came bundled with my genes. My early childhood in rural Zululand imbued me with a great love for the sky and all the tantalising promise that shines down upon us no matter what we do. As a four-year-old, I dreamt of flying close to the birds and the stars, and I still do. When the time came for me to enrich my education at university level, I tentatively questioned some of the concepts I was being taught in astrophysics, but not for a moment did I challenge the method being used. Mathematics was god, and my fluency gave me an unfair advantage, an inside track to success that I would not easily forego. I was hooked.

Ironically, salvation came courtesy of a particle physicist, a man so steeped in the magic of theoretical physics that he represented in its entirety the school of thought I was ultimately to reject. Professor Steven Weinberg at the University of Texas is a mensch. I salute him with the same reverence that I salute Richard Feynman. Although they both, each in his own way, epitomised the religion of mathematical science, they remained real; they recognised the real world as a constraint on our theorising. At some significant but undeclared level, they were engineers. They were problem solvers. I so regret that I never got to meet Feynman, but I did come under the direct influence of Weinberg, and it is thus fitting that I give him the credit for my recovery. Dr Weinberg left me with abiding mantras, the greatest of which is that no theory is sacrosanct. There ought to be no sacred cows in the practice of physical science, and by Jove, that was something that really rattled my cage.

Although it seems unfair to select just a handful of illuminating influences on my life when so many giants lent me their shoulders, I must acknowledge the unequivocal role played by my late father in bringing me to the keyboard to write this book. A physicist and amateur mechanic, my father serviced and repaired every machine within the ambit of our frontier homestead, just for the love of it. That respect for mechanical precision lives in me still, a watchmaker's heaven I immerse myself in every day of my life. My father presented me the basics: Imagine you are building a bridge over the sea, and that lives depend on it; first reduce everything to real-world first principles and proceed logically from there; and finally, *no hocus pocus*.

It took decades for his self-evident wisdom to kick in and start to constrain the way I practise science. Unsurprisingly, during those formative years, I reserved any life-changing advice for the ideas and theories of others, keeping my own preconceptions intact. I carried on regardless, doing blindingly complicated mathematics and calling it physics, quite oblivious to the looming schism between what I had been taught and what my instruments were showing me. I'm not sure exactly what forced the hairline crack to finally fracture, but it came at about the time I was reading up on the notorious Copenhagen debates between Albert Einstein and Niels Bohr. By then, I had already found grave difficulty with Einstein's relativity theories, and was at once both puzzled and amazed by the 180-degree turn-around in Einstein's basic world view when he came to cross swords with Niels Bohr. The details of that particular drama must be postponed for another time, I'm afraid, because we need to stay on track here. The key point is that my transformation came from none other than Albert Einstein himself, in the rebuttal of the black hole theory he proffered in those debates.

My career in astrophysics was built upon notions that most people have never heard of, or if they have, they know next to nothing about. Although I am going to spend the next few paragraphs discussing cosmology, I must admit that I don't like cosmology, as you shall no doubt soon realise. This brief interlude is unavoidable because cosmology is where the absurdity first became apparent. Specifically, it was the cosmological model attributed to Albert Einstein that exposed the holes in his socks.

Two things puzzled me about Albert Einstein's conception of the cosmos: Firstly, he controversially conceptualised the universe as eternal and non-expanding; and secondly, he earnestly argued against the existence of black holes. Why was I puzzled? Because both of these things — universal expansion and so-called Schwarzschild singularities, upon which black hole theory is premised — are derivations (and not very good ones at that) of his own *magnum opus*, the general relativity theory. Expansion and singularities are properties that emerge from solutions to the field equations of general relativity, and as such, should have been accepted by the author of the theory, surely? But they were not. He rejected them, and tried very hard to change the rest of the world's mindset in that regard. He failed dismally on both counts.

I shan't tax you with the formal intricacies of the first of these two conundrums, for they reside in a tangled chaos called differential geometry and tensor analysis. I shouldn't think anyone in their right mind would voluntarily venture there. But when it came to the second of these two puzzles, Einstein used logical analysis that was stunning in its simplicity. Einstein rebutted black hole singularities using one indefatigable argument: No matter how elegant the formalism that suggested them, singularities could not be realised in reality. We cannot, said Einstein to his audience at Princeton in 1932, simply assume that matter can be arbitrarily compressed by any force whatsoever so that it is reduced to zero volume and infinite density. *Quod erat demonstrandum.* How absolutely marvellous. Suddenly, I realised in all its glory what my late father had so patiently tried to teach me. Keep it *real*.

Let me be perfectly clear: *I am an astrophysicist who does not believe in Big Bang theory.* The point to be made — and underlined twice in red ink — is this: I reject the Big Bang model because I have found no compelling reason to accept that the hypotheses being presented by the model are reflections of objective reality. I have not become a convert to the Big Bang doctrine because my understanding of scientific principles tells me it remains no more than elaborate but unsubstantiated conjecture. I do not criticise the standard model because it conflicts with my belief in another model. I must stress this point quite vigorously; because when all is said and done, it is actually my cosmological agnosticism that qualifies me to write this book.

Ergo, I do not question Islam because I am a Christian; I do not critique Christianity because I am a Jew; I do not deny Mayan doomsday ideas because they conflict with my belief in Nostradamus; I do not challenge Greenpeace because I am a member of the National Rifle Association; and I do not attack the 9/11 conspiracy theories because I am a Republican. In every case, I assess those beliefs using the objective scientific method, and in every case I find them wanting. And I remain in each instance an agnostic.

I do hold one personal axiom that I must nevertheless offer here, and that is my take on reality and truth. In seeking to prevent subjectivity from undermining pure knowledge, we are essentially trying to remove our entire species from the equation. We are of course a vitally important part of the universe we contemplate, but in order to evaluate knowledge without the prejudicial bias of personal opinion, we need to define a pristine benchmark where all things are as they are existentially, exempt from mental shading. That's the ideal — a cosmos without little people making up theories and playing mind games.

It gives us something to aim at, in the full knowledge that perfection cannot be achieved in practice. Thus, as biologists we can approach this ideal in studying a tree mechanically, identifying inter alia its component parts and observing how they interact with each other, and how the organism reacts to and feeds the environment in which it lives. There would still no doubt be a level of assumption involved, but the cause-and-effect, mechanistic purity of our method keeps it to a minimum.

When we take our study to another level, say for example considering a tree as part of the chain of interconnected, developing organisms proposed by Darwinian evolution, we start to dabble in belief.[3] The tenets of evolutionary theory can of course be tested empirically in an ongoing quest to validate the philosophical frame that encloses the fossil evidence, but we should not forget that the embracing theory is imagined, not seen. It is a way to increase confidence, but not to achieve absolute certainty. As soon as we have no doubt whatsoever that our opinion is unmitigated truth, we are believers, insulated by our own faith.

I'd like to add another point: In all my books I have nailed my colours to the mast — I use classical mechanics and empirical physics as the tools of my enquiry, and I do so precisely because those techniques are inherently constrained from attempting a "theory of everything". A mechanical approach can go only as far as analysing cause and effect, with the caveat that it succeeds in inverse proportion to remoteness (that is, it works best locally).

By its nature, scientific pragmatism tacitly sets realistic boundaries to our field of enquiry. There can be no attempt to contrive an overarching explanation of all things. That is in any case not the business of science. The empirical

---

3 I call this class of model a *hypostack*, a contraction of the words *hypothesis* and *stack*.

scientific method can be applied to only observed aspects of our natural environment, and depends on how well we make that initial observation. The higher the image's resolution at level one, the greater our confidence may be in the realism of each succeeding step. We start where we are and work our way outwards. It's the only sensible way to achieve robust results.

If we follow this suggested path, we shall soon realise that we don't need those strange, sometimes irrational methodologies that are frequently used to unravel the inner threads of the phenomena we study. I was delighted to find that I did not, in forty years of hands-on astrophysics, ever need to invoke Einstein's relativity, quantum mechanics, or Sheldrake's morphic field. We can do science much more simply than that, if only we keep it real and confine ourselves to observed phenomena. And then we step back and apply Ockham's razor.[4] But what then of invisible atoms, you might ask?

Of course we need to project our minds forward, beyond what we can see, and then wait for our instruments to catch up. I'm not such a reactionary fool as to suggest that we limit our thinking absolutely and finally to what we can see. All I'm saying is that we should not get too far ahead of ourselves and our factual base. In 1900, it seemed perfectly reasonable for astronomers to suggest that stars would likely organise themselves into far grander structures than our solar system. Thirty years later, advances in telescope optics revealed the existence of galaxies. In 1930, astronomers

---

4 Ockham's razor: a technique in interpreting empirical results, whereby the simpler of competing explanations is preferred.

looking at galaxies were quite right to speculate about galaxy clusters. In less than twenty years, their prophecies were realised when clusters were observed.

The same holds true at micro level. It seemed obvious that what we can see and touch is composed of smaller building blocks, and a couple of thousand years ago, the hypothetical creature was even given a name — the *atom*. During the Second World War, that theory was put to the test when nuclear fission was tamed for human use. Although atoms had still never been seen, the Bohr model's predictions were met with astounding results. It was only in late 2013 that microscopy finally reached the point where an atom could actually be photographed. Today, we apparently have evidence from particle accelerators that suggests that the components of atomic nuclei (protons and neutrons) have even smaller parts, and we have no reason to assume that it ends there.

The natural limitations of scientific pragmatism insist that we should speculate as little as possible beyond what we can achieve with our experiments. Preferably, for purposes of engineering our explanations of real things, we ought to go no further than one level beyond the conclusion of our empirical results. If we continue to add layers upon layers of imagined phenomena, we are building a hypo-stack, and that, my friends, is a house of cards. It was a jolly good thing that fine scientific minds applied themselves systematically to the creation of the atomic model. So was the musing of early astronomers about galaxies. But here's the thing: Extrapolating from that alone the notion that the universe propagates by a green elephant laying radio-active eggs in black holes is just too much of a stretch.

Making that elephant model a law compulsory for all scholars in the field would be even greater injustice. We would be well advised to heed my Dad's words on the subject: *Keep it real.*

We should not, as a matter of principle, have such a thing as cosmology, at least not in science. By its very nature, cosmology belongs more appropriately to the realm of religious philosophy, and should play no part in the practice of physical science. In a nutshell, we can profitably apply reason only to a world that is reasonable, rational, and appreciable.

We humans are taxed with an overbearing desire to be right. It so influences our thinking that one might with some merit suggest that our beliefs are shaped almost entirely by the imperitive to establish and maintain the dominance of our opinions. Belief as a syndrome is characterised by subconscious censorship to such a degree that it ultimately becomes the primary drive behind egotism. Since we all present this drive naturally and in abundance, how can the ideal of objective science be reached? By what means and to what degree can I attain objectivity in my thesis?

I must remind myself continuously that I too am a product of the system. My education, though excellent, was nevertheless overtly conventional. I came out of it neat and tidy and ready for duty. In the unforgiving postgraduate world where I was expected to apply my knowledge usefully to the satisfaction of my benefactors, I slowly came to realise that education was really a form of classical conditioning in the Pavlovian mode; we were its dogs, and both the tricks we were to perform and the rewards we would consequently receive were made clear to us all. It was also clear that the only way to fruitfully develop a career in the sciences was to toe the party line. Although I managed to do as I was told and gratefully pocketed the change, I was a worried man. How was science to progress if results were validated solely by their fit to a preferred theoretical model, and were not tested against unbiased reality?

Beliefs are a comfortable overcoat in this frantic world. They create in us a feel-good condition that we are extremely loath to let go. They play a crucial part in building and reinforcing our self-esteem. They form a matrix of presets in the mind's eye, and are subtle enough to allow us to merrily hit the Like button on Facebook before we've read much more than a post's heading or identified the sender's name, or to click Forward for an e-mail broadcast without first verifying the message it contains. The irresponsible naivety of these habits stems from a perfectly natural tendency to *like* what we believe and from our desire to align ourselves with the attractive moral code that our superficial scan imbues in the message. We see a picture of a puppy or a melting glacier or the outstretched arms of Jesus, and we immediately lose our faculty for intelligent discrimination. We simply go ahead and vote with our mouse button. Anyone who participates in cyber media will have been spammed umpteen times, and will be able to recognise the behaviour pattern a mile off. But when we are spammed, does our annoyance persuade us to stop doing it ourselves? Not likely. The primary polarity in the science of irrational knowledge is simply "my belief versus the rest".

It is fairly easy to recognise the good common sense that underpins my thesis, and to buy wholeheartedly into the scheme I propose for the renormalisation of the scientific method. I can see my scheme of scientific pragmatism already being slung with relish at the precious theories of friend and foe across the chasm of cyberspace. We seem to have a fascination with the breaking down of structures — witness the ghoulish crowds that gather to watch the implosive demolition of downtown high-rise buildings — and the Internet's protective moat grants us free reign to attack and break the ideas of others with impunity. It is quite clear that when it comes to a critical appraisal of beliefs, we limit our unbridled enthusiasm to attacking those of others; we make of our own beliefs always the exception. And therein lies the rub.

There are some principles that I shall drum into the text by repetition; and arguably, the most important of these involves the way to absorb this book most profitably. My long-suffering reader will no doubt frequently come to passages and ideas that cause her to pause and evaluate; I would be satisfied with nothing less. However, for reasons that should become obvious as we go along — if indeed they are not obvious already — I must insist that the evaluation not be performed in the light of the reader's own personal beliefs. Objectivity is of paramount importance. If you're Christian, and an example I use confronts your own Christian faith, bear in mind that I merely illustrate a point; weigh it up against the demonstration of dogma by Muslims or Scientologists or some other belief system. I shall say no more at this stage; it is a given that I'll offend the convictions of each and every reader at places in the book, and my concern is that a clash with personal faith will cause you to bale out before the narrative is complete.

Even the most objectively real tenets of science arise from a subjective base: our primary assumptions. The success of my mission will depend largely upon my ability to convince my readers to accept and adopt my own assumptions, and to proceed as if they were axioms. I'm asking you, for the tiniest fraction of a nanosecond, to believe along with me; then we'll be free to at long last get on with some reality physics and avoid a misty detour into the fanciful, entrancing fjords of unconstrained imagination.

Scientific pragmatism articulates a method whereby we extrapolate from data with minimum pollution from belief. We shall never be rid of belief; it's an instinct welded into our cells. We can however significantly reduce the bias of our prejudicial presets whilst we are busy uncovering the basics. To do that, we need to understand what objective truth is. It then becomes far less onerous to understand belief, recognise it in our own world view, and find a way to set it aside while we lay the foundations of a scientific model. Thereafter, we do with the information what we will; human nature and instinctive egotism will no doubt always play their part, but at least our blackboard will be clear of half-erased nuances at the outset. The very last thing I would want to do is replace an existing dominant paradigm with another paradigm that I prefer.

Let's get down to basics: Science seeks to reveal truth in the world about us, truth is unadorned reality, and reality is that which exists independently of any observer. All that stands between us and an accurate vision of reality is a belief-sodden mind. Our individual mindset will always be intransigently geocentric, anthropocentric, and egocentric. We each have a unique point of view, and our personal vision of the world is unlike any other. The great challenge facing us is the necessity, for a brief moment, to step outside of our mental walls. We have to try to imagine a cosmos with no sentient beings. That unsullied, pristine, universal engine, endless wheels within wheels on a scale so utterly gargantuan that even atoms become monsters, is where truth lies. If we're to understand the nature of truth, we need to try to picture a world with no thoughts, no interpretation, and no mental colour. Of course, we all need our minds and the rational frames of reference they bring to our fleeting existence, but the truth we seek in the present campaign is not what we think it is, nor what we believe it is, but what it is, irrespective of our paltry opinions.

Earlier this evening, I went out into my garden to spend some time gazing upwards at the firmament rolling almost imperceptibly across the darkened sky. It's my reality check. I looked at the stars and reminded myself that they are real stars, burning orbs that sent a radiant image of themselves my way, and that I happened to look up and catch a few minutes of that celestial generosity tonight. It's so easy to paint a romantic picture in our mind's eye of things that lie tantalisingly beyond our reach; if we could but resolve more detail, we would expose the illusion that they are merely points of light decorating the celestial sphere.

Stars are real things, every one of them far bigger than our Earth, and unimaginably hotter. They possess a vast range of physical properties not nearly obvious to the naked eye, and in our ignorance we create Christmas trees up there in the heavens. Astrology and other superstitions of that ilk are testimony to the kind of mental movie we make up about stars, and that we have managed to get away with simply because they are too far away for us to see properly. The Achilles' heel of this imaginative method of describing actuality is that it's a slippery slope. It commences by addressing a cosmic mystery with nothing more than a little white lie, and all too soon it escalates into a fully fledged, multitiered belief paradigm, replete with mesmerising black holes, dark energies, and Noah's arks.

I am once again indoors, sitting at my computer. The stars continue to send their messages our way, as they did when I was outside gazing at them, and as they have for all the aeons before humans existed on Earth, and as they shall no doubt continue to do after our species is extinct. Reality exists irrespectively of your or my existence. It exists independently of both our perception of the world and of our subjective interpretation of what we see and experience. If all sentient beings were to die out, there would still be a vast universe out there and in here, cycling through its tireless phases regardless.

The ultimate grail of our faltering odyssey in science is a shared understanding of that remote, isolated environment outside of our heads. When we observe or experience something, the inbound signal passes through our mental filter, and by associative logic, we create a comfortable image of it in our mind's eye. The mental filter adds colour to the signal, and in so doing creates distance between our understanding and the naked truth. Reality is pristine; our minds add the bias. The aim of science is to strip away as much of that mental camouflage as we possibly can, so we can see and understand the ungilded lily that sent us the signal in the first place.

What has happened in practice is quite the opposite. We have quite simply fallen in love with our mind and our imagination to such a degree that we now declare, without shame, that reality is a matter of opinion, that it is observer defined, intrinsically different for each varying point of view. Well, I'm here to tell you that the individual reality idea is utter nonsense. If we are going to nail down the compromising effect of belief in our quest for truth, then we must, as an urgent necessity, realise that reality is not what we *think* it is, but what it *actually* is. That's why it's called reality.

Psychiatrist Dr Thomas Szasz nailed it: *"If you talk to God, you are praying. If God talks to you, you have schizophrenia."* If a chap wanders down the road declaring that he's a cucumber sandwich, that's not his version of reality; it's his version of delusion.

The truth, and indeed the principles of physical science intended to reveal truth, ought not to be dependent upon consensus. Something is not made true simply because we agree with one another. On this one point, politics and science are clearly divided, and sit at opposite poles of discussion. Consensus may be deeply ingrained in the ethos of democracy, but it is entirely inconsequential in a physics classroom. Or at least it should be. But sadly, politics, majority rule, and personal greed have crept into science as well, to science's lasting detriment. As we shall see in the pages yet to come, mass agreement is a sociological phenomenon, and expresses nothing more important than shared belief. It is wholly subjective, and we need to remind ourselves constantly that we are striving for untainted objectivity, quite another thing altogether.

Crucially then, we test the principles of democracy against beliefs most commonly held in the tribe, while we validate the tenets of science against reality itself. No matter what we believe about gravitation, irrespective of the words we use to describe it, and taking no account at all of what we would like gravitation to be, we can test it, all of us, by jumping off the garden shed. Impartial gravitation pays no heed to our philosophical persuasion. We hit the ground equally, and that's what we urgently need to take note of before we get lost in a maze of dreams. We can stop for tea right now and give the above paragraph time to embed itself in our minds. It's that important.

The aim of scientific endeavour is to progressively illuminate the truth, and ensure our opinions about nature align as closely as possible with virgin reality. The operative word is *progressively*. Science is accomplished always in small steps on a journey from the near to the far. The way I see it, science is explicitly precluded from whole answers, from any form or shape of cosmology or theory of everything. The "whole truth" ethos is better suited to the realms of religion and abstract philosophy, where free imagination reigns unchallenged by objective reality. Look at it this way — scientific investigations examine finite chunks of an infinitely extensive data field. These infinitesimals become the quanta of our knowledge, and we use them to draw the universe as a paint-by-numbers exercise on an endless canvas. We can use knowledge successfully like a fog lamp to help us peer through the mists that surround us, but no matter how clever a light we employ, it is never able to shine through all the veils of mystery that lie between our point of view and the ends of the observable universe. All we can do, really, is reduce the blurring effect our own beliefs have on the view.

There exists a certain class of student — I can after years at the rock face spot them a mile away — with the inclination to reduce all argument to semantics, and who will leap upon this assertion to trash it rhetorically because the truth, they say, is no more than a subjective opinion. No, it is not. Truth is constant, unconcerned, and invariable. The only variables are what we believe about the truth, and how we interpret it to fit our personally preferred paradigm.

This philosophy shapes both my mindset and my scientific method. As an approach to life, it requires a certain discipline in the analysis of information. The goal would be for systematic scientific pragmatism to become habitual. If it is second nature to us, then the battle is nearly won. First though, we must reduce the incoming froth to first principles. This is not easy, but we must do the best we can. We shall be discussing this in more detail as we proceed, but it is crucial to understand already that our conception of first principles will always rest upon our assumptions. No matter how well we succeed in cutting through the fat of belief, there will *always* be a layer of subjectivity separating our world view from the unvarnished truth. Our aim therefore is not to eliminate subjectivity (that seems impossible anyway), but to reduce it to the barest practicable minimum.

If we are to succeed, we must first hold a few primary assumptions in common. These are that the universe is without finite bounds, that the natural environment exists independently of any observer or its thoughts, and that we must use logic and rational thought in our analysis. First principles are determined in terms of these few axioms.

I reiterate: The first step is to reduce the information bundle to first principles, as best we can, in the light of our foundational assumptions. This is useful inasmuch as it immediately cuts through the distortions of any theoretical model we might prefer to utilise. Quite apart from its doctrinal influences, model-dependent analysis almost inevitably wastes an enormous amount of time and effort. If our aim is to conserve a preferred model, we must try continuously to find fault in measurements that don't fit the model, laboriously develop new physics and mathematical techniques to bring anomalous measurements into alignment with the model, and time and again paddle back to our starting point from dead ends that result from our failing to validate information that appears at first glance to support our original bias.

Once we have extracted and isolated first principles from the measurements, we look for recognisable patterns in terms of fundamental physics. Everything in nature seems to be affected by spin, and spin is a consequence of polarity, so the first thing I look for is the obvious existence of polarity. And here we need to talk about cats and dogs.

Isn't it strange that when you tell people that you like cats, they invariably assume you don't like dogs? That liking tea automatically gets taken to mean you dislike coffee? That being gay somehow implies you're anti-straight? I call this the cat-and-dog rule — the baseless assumption of polarity in opinions. It stems from the misconception that polarity is caused by prejudice.

We can generalise the cat-and-dog rule in this way: Belief in theory A does not render opposing theory B untrue. A crucial part of the discipline we exercise in studying belief is the clear separation of belief and truth. In identifying or even defining belief, we need make no mention of truth at all. What's more, it is this very principle that dictates that we should not, as scientists, include our own belief structures in the investigation process. That would unavoidably contaminate the study with our personal subjectivity. Thus, for example, if the person studying belief is a Christian, he leaves Christianity out of his list of case studies (and the same would apply if he were atheist, Muslim, Big Banger, Mayan calendar disciple, etc.).

Once our research (or for that matter, the reading of this book) is complete and we can intuitively grasp the fundamentals it reveals, we should then — *and only then* — apply those principles to our own belief paradigm to see where that takes us. Be prepared for shock and incredulity.

Another very important constraint offered by scientific pragmatism is the reining-in of mania. Manic expression has a way of convincing people that is both puzzling and alarming. The rise of Nazi Germany from the ashes of the Great War could not have happened without a play on emotional heartstrings and offering the suffering mass some hope that what they secretly wished for could indeed be realised. Would Nazism ever have happened on anything like the scale it eventually did without Hitler's oratorical style and rhetoric? Can you envisage a seething mass of blindly cheering hopefuls in Munich if Adolf Hitler had come before them and said in a quiet, timid voice, "You know, chaps, you really ought to consider becoming National Socialists"?

So why do I say it is puzzling? Prior to embarking upon my research for this book, I was confused by the fact that bespittled rhetoric fails more than it succeeds; but when it does work, it's absolutely spectacular. It occurred to me that it is not the rhetoric *per se* that gets people going; it is actually more likely to switch them off. A positive response from the audience depends entirely upon the orator pulling an emotional trigger in prejudicial, pre-existing belief in those listening to him. If the message fails to stimulate a pre-existing emotional need in the listener, it will flop. Whichever way it goes, it is completely independent of the degree of truth in the message being broadcast.

While I was writing *The Virtue of Heresy*, I passed the draft manuscript out to some friends to review and criticise. One response startled me. "Hilton," she said to me, "I like it, it's generally well written, but one thing puts me off reading it, and that's your obsessive use of exclamation marks. I know you're passionate about your message, but you should seriously consider not using that level of emphasis at all. Let the facts speak for themselves."

Those wise words probably saved my book from abject failure.

I talk and do research based on a framework of ideals. These in effect express my ethics. However, one has to tread carefully here; ideals are goals, and in my experience are seldom, if ever, attainable in the real world. Thus, I declare that the goal of scientific endeavour is the illumination of pure, objective truth. It is a goal, something to aim at, and implies a standard yet to be realised in reality — the perfectly objective scientist. I see it as setting the bar in terms of my ethical approach, expressing a secular morality, and — here is the thing — it needs to be seen in the context of my human fallibility. Any scientific investigation proceeds always from primary assumptions, and these are really a declaration of one's bias at the outset. In a nutshell: for as long as I'm human, I can never attain complete synchronicity with pure truth. My personal beliefs make sure of that. But I can sure as heck make truth my goal in life.

No matter what my personal beliefs may or may not be, I have always maintained that religion has no place in science. Faith in God has its own place, and its own way of exploring reality to find meaning. Indeed, I have no problem with religionists using science as an element in their internal debates — provided of course that they do not twist the science to fit their argument. But the reverse is patently unacceptable to me. Science is secular and should remain independent of any and all theological models.

I'm not worried about belief *per se*. What concerns me is how belief colours our thinking and manifests itself in aberrant ways. There is nothing disturbing about a young lady going to mosque and praying to Allah and immersing herself in readings of the Quran, although as it happens, I believe in the divinity of none of those things. Notwithstanding my personal scepticism, I consider that kind of behaviour humane and all to the good. What does disturb me, and profoundly so, is when the beliefs so obtained translate into a state of mind that produces suicide bombers. This may be an extreme example, but the principle is clear. Belief influences our daily lives in every conceivable way, contaminating even a supposedly objective practice like physical science.

And that, my friend, includes my beliefs and yours.

It is more often from pride than from ignorance that we are so obstinately opposed to current opinions; we find the first places taken, and we do not want to be the last.

Francois De La Rochefoucauld, moralist (1613–1680)

The history of science is of as much interest to me as the scientific method. As a secular scholar, I find rich grounds for research in the way the Roman Catholic Church has approached matters of science. My personal view is that church and state should be separated from one another, and so should church and science. They belong in different classrooms. Science should be independent of religion, just as religion functions perfectly well without science. Many eminent and able scholars in various fields, notably astronomy, have been Roman Catholics. But they ruined their good work, in my opinion, by filtering it through a haze of doctrine and ideology. As a result, they've managed to shoot themselves in the foot a good many times. Don't get me wrong, I don't deny anyone the right to look at the cosmos in whichever way suits them, but in the common body of knowledge known as science, there is no place for religious interpretation. That belongs in another room, another quest. Just close your eyes for a moment and imagine we were compelled to do physics through the eyes of Scientology. Pretty much everyone except Scientologists would be appalled.

I am not talking about religionism or theistic belief necessarily, just plain belief. By *belief* I mean a conviction obtained by means other than rational deduction from first principles.

Let's discuss the notion of reality, because it is fundamental to definitions being put forward in this work. I believe in an external (non-mind) reality, independent of your or my existence. Although Albert Einstein asserted that time is a perception, no more than the local function of a clock, and that reality is observer defined, I must disagree. Timothy Leary's clinical experiments with LSD provide an interesting analogue. During an acid trip, all rational constraints (like time) are dismantled, and for a while, the tripper's perception of the universe is truly existential. Then he wakes up, and lo and behold, the real world is still there, warts and all. What the tripper believed was true was transient, unlike the independent reality that remained regardless. We can go into free fall and believe that gravity doesn't exist, but sooner or later we hit Earth again.

Now, let's settle the thorny issue of time. It's one of life's great mysteries, and we need to accept it for what it is rather than try to understand it intellectually. Time belongs in the same boat as infinity — we can't get our mind around it or express the principles logically from first cause, but that doesn't mean it does not exist. Time may well be intangible, but it certainly exists, and it affects our lives every bit as actually as gravitation does. Time is the unidirectional, irreversible sequence of events, and we measure its progress by counting off the regular cycles of nature. If time were not real, as some very clever theoretical physicists are suggesting, then we would not age. In fact, if time was not a real parameter of existence, there could be no such thing as a regular oscillation anyway. We may not like it, just as we dislike gravity when we're pedalling uphill, but that's no good reason to deny it. Time *is* real, it affects us in real, tangible ways, and we must learn to deal with it.

That brings us to the matter of scale. Whilst I do accept that Homo sapiens is my native species, and that we all share this planet with one another, I have been involved in astronomy so long now that I find it difficult to pull my mind back to this scale of events and make it important enough to worry about.

All of human thinking is constrained by two essential parameters — scale and frame of reference. We need somehow to take a step back and try to grasp the bigger picture. If our forefathers hadn't managed to do that, we would no doubt have continued to labour under the visually compelling illusion that the Sun and the stars orbit around a stationary flat Earth.

Our little history is not even a blink of the galaxy's eye. If I were to draw a scale line across the blackboard to represent the entire time that the species Homo sapiens has existed on Earth (call it one hundred thousand years for easy maths), and if I let that line be one metre long, and then I extend the line on the same scale so that it represented the lifespan of the Earth itself (call it five billion years for easy maths), then the blackboard would need to be *fifty thousand kilometres wide* to accommodate the line. The equatorial circumference of the Earth is about forty thousand kilometres, which means my blackboard would wrap right around the planet and then some; human beings would fill just one lonely metre.

Let's take it a step further. If we were to let our one-metre chalk line represent just the amount of time that man has had civilisation, technology, and written language (we'll call that ten thousand years for easy maths), the blackboard would need to be *five hundred thousand kilometres* wide for the line representing the age of the Earth to fit. It would stretch from my classroom to way, way beyond the Moon. The entire history of our civilisation would take up just one metre.

To say we are small fry, on both space and time axes, is a ludicrous understatement. There are greater and more wonderful things in the universe than human beings; deal with it.

Although we have touched on the notion of civilisation, it remains something of a hot potato in this debate. Liberals seem to despise it as much as conservatives canonise it. Liberals reduce the argument immediately to definitions of the word; conservatives lock and load. To me, and this is crucial to my general argument, civilisation is a measure of how well we suppress and control our baser instincts. Civilisation represents finer ideals, and is the discipline we would expect when humankind expresses its ability, unique amongst all known creatures, to practice noble, abstract thought.

Sadly, noble thought is an ephemeral grace. My nobleness dies with me, and my children do not inherit it with their genes. Any righteousness they may have will have been taught to them by their social peers, most effectively by their parents. As far as we can tell, it is not something that is constrained by the genome, and it operates from that small sliver of the psyche that houses our free will. We are not going to evolve into noble creatures; we are going to evolve into a tribe aligned with our chemical destiny. The crocodile is not going to evolve into a vegetarian, or at least, not because it has an ethical objection to killing wildebeests. We flow with gravity, like a river tortuously sidestepping the high ground over millennia in blind obedience to its design paradigm. Our chemical template rules.

Our social purpose is the preservation and passing on of civilisation. It runs counter to the cellular imperative in our veins, which uses a heady cocktail of pleasurable nerve ends and fear factors to keep the herd tightly bound and fruitful. Nevertheless, human beings have the capacity to move beyond mere survival physics to embark upon a life journey that is to some degree selfless and requires sacrifice and empathy. I don't mean selfless in the sense that ants are selfless; ants simply obey the code in their cells, and are really just pseudo individuals, atoms of a greater organism. Selflessness in human animals requires that we contain our raging instincts and do some good. There are few who do this well; sadly, many of those who do try to be civilised, do it to such an extreme that they end up no better than a crocodile. They become merely the opposing pole in a tribal balancing act. To sum up: the notion of the noble savage is a dastardly myth, and runs counter to everything I'm trying so hard to convey in these pages.

I am a scientist. I follow the classical, empirical scientific method in order to unravel the wonders of nature — firstly, awareness, experience, observation, and experiment; then analysis of those results; then the formulation of a hypothesis to suggest a cause and predict effects; and finally, peer evaluation, testing, and criticism of the hypothesis leading either to declaration of a theory or a law, or modification or even abandonment of the hypothesis. Observation is the kick-off point, and remains always *fait accompli*; what we make of it is variable. A model constructed following the empirical scientific method starts in external reality and ends in external reality. Pure thought lies somewhere in between.

Sir Isaac Newton represents the single greatest influence on the way I do physics. I'd like to share with you some reflections on Newton before we go any further. A complex, abrasive character, Isaac Newton was never much given to social charm and wit. Although he is best remembered for his laws of motion and gravitation — and, I suppose, even more famously for the unsubstantiated legend of an accidental collision between his head and a falling apple — as a citizen of those darkly amusing times in England's history, he was much, much more than just gravitation and an apple. He was, after all, a devout Christian. It surprises many to learn that Isaac Newton published far more in the field of theology than in physics. He was in addition obsessed with the barren art of alchemy. This too may astonish you, but the author of the classic *Principia Mathematica* devoted significantly more laboratory time to the futile goal of converting base metals to gold than to quantifying motion and mass.

What astounded me, so much so that I dedicated my career to the physics of Isaac Newton, was that these strongly dominant quirks in his psychological makeup did nothing to impede his incredible objectivity when it came to systematically revealing laws of physics that survived four hundred years of scientific progress without losing an iota of applicability. Newton did not let his personal beliefs interfere with his explanation of reality. He makes no mention at all of the supernatural in *Principia Mathematica* or his later work *Opticks*, although he spent the greater part of his life in pursuit of it. Nor did Isaac Newton concern himself with what causes gravity. He was interested only in how it affects our lives and the world around us. What's more, he provided us the tools to build rockets and explore outerspace centuries before technology finally allowed us to go there.

We cannot possibly exaggerate the importance of Newton's example to the progress of science. Despite being a deeply religious man with some quaintly metaphysical hobbies, Isaac Newton was able to practise physics more purely than anyone else in history. That he could so objectively set aside his philosophical convictions to look at the world as a material machine in conventional space sets him apart from his peers, in my opinion. We might infer from his approach to physics what could have been Newton's zeroth law — that the success of physical science in describing truth is inversely proportional to the application of belief by the scientist.[5] The rest of my book is focussed single-mindedly on exploring this assertion and the implications it has for humanity.

One of the aspects I find most compelling about astronomy is that the stars don't care. I can remember so clearly the moment this thought first occurred to me as a child, while I gazed up at the bejewelled night sky of my beloved Zululand. I realised that they are so remote in every respect that nothing I or any of my tribe could do — no matter how

---

5 The notion of a zeroth law comes from thermodynamics, where the fundamental law occurred to scientists after laws one, two, and three had already been cast in stone.

profound, tragic, noble, graceful, or funny — would cause them to blink back one tear. Or smile. Or give a damn. My arrival in the arena of survival is as inconsequential to the objects of my study as my inevitable departure will some-day be. In the big scheme, I am nearly nothing; so close to infinitely trivial as makes no difference. I can try to be a big fish in a small pond and bask in the applause, but I should know that the stars are not going to blink. They have much more important things to attend to. And that's good to know.

From there, it just got curiouser and curiouser, and like Alice, I decided to take my tea in Wonderland.

A casual stroll through the lunatic asylum shows that faith does not prove anything.

FRIEDRICH NIETZSCHE

Julius Schnorr von Carolsfeld, Creation, Die Bibel in Bildern. 1860

To the scientific mind, belief systems are crazy; they revolve around paranormal or extra-normal phenomena. But they also have an internal justification mechanism. On their own terms, they are legitimate, and tend to consider their doctrines to be an expression of profound wisdom. The "Word of God" is a rubber stamp for anything.

3

SCIENCE IS AS
SCIENCE DOES

Faith without works

HOW, I WONDER, DID I ever become involved in astro-physics? The question is easily answered, and I shall; but it also leads tantalisingly to the more important question that ultimately forms the foundation for this book — how did I manage to escape, almost unscathed, from the seduc-tive grasp of *metaphysics*, when it seemed that all about me the doyens of science were falling like dominoes into the trap? That's a more difficult question to answer truth-fully. As mentioned before, I owe my freedom above all to my late father, who would time and again punctuate his marvellous explanations of the natural world with the stern admonition, "No *hocus-pocus, my boy, no hocus-pocus*".

A foundation of my thesis is that belief flows in our veins. We all have it, and scientists, for all their bleating protest, are not exempt. I am ever grateful to Michael Shermer for fearlessly breaking the ground before I came along with *Socks*; he makes my mission so much easier to accomplish.

> I take this one step further to argue that even these different models of physics and cosmology used by scientists to explain, say, light as a particle or light as a wave, are themselves beliefs, and when coupled to higher-order theories about physics, mathematics, and cosmology, form entire world views about nature, and therefore belief-dependent realism is a higher-order form of model-dependent realism. *On top of this, our brains place a judgement value upon beliefs.* There are good evolutionary reasons why we form beliefs and judge them as good or bad that I will discuss in the chapter on political beliefs, but suffice it to say here that our evolved tribal tendencies lead us to form coalitions with fellow like-minded members of our group *and to demonise others who hold different beliefs*. Thus, when we hear about the beliefs of others that differ from our own, we are naturally inclined to dismiss or dismantle their beliefs as nonsense, evil, or both. This propensity makes it even more difficult to change our minds in the teeth of new evidence.[1]

The emphasis is mine. That we award an almost moralistic judgement value to a school of thought that we fortuitously subscribe to, and proceed to denigrate the

---

1 Michael Shermer, *The Believing Brain* (New York: Times Books, 2011).

opinions and even the characters of those who choose another path is a blight upon the perspicuity with which we ought to be expressing ourselves. There is no room in physics for political posturing and arrogance, but I'll be damned if we don't ignore the ideals and do science in the style of playground bullies.

Theories do indeed become laws, when men make them so. Thus they move from some degree of scientific conjecture, to tenets of a fully fledged belief system. The flaw in the system is starkly illuminated by this: A theory is "well substantiated, well supported" only by prior theories that have been canonised into law by influential people. It's called a *science-by-standard model*. Contemporary science (like religion) trades perilously upon sanctity of opinions and mystery of arcane jargon.

Standard models are multitiered theoretical constructs that supposedly help to make the process of scientific discovery more efficient. And they would, if only they were proven true; but in practice, they remain just self-supporting, high-rise hypotheses.

Professor Jim Peebles's classic text *The Principles of Physical Cosmology* has become a standard reference in theoretical astrophysics. In the preface to that book, Peebles addresses some remarks to the question of standard models:

> There is ambiguity about what is meant by the 'standard model' in cosmology: in everyday use it can refer to the well-established elements of the theory, or to plausible but speculative attempts to fill in details ... The use of the word 'model' is appropriate,

because the picture is known to be an incomplete approximation to what is really happening, and there certainly is the chance that there is something very wrong with the picture. The word 'standard' is meant to signify that it has survived an impressive variety of nontrivial tests that have left no known credible alternatives.[2]

There is ambiguity not only about the standard model itself, but also how it should properly handle dissent. On the one hand, Peebles admits that models are incomplete approximations of reality, yet on the other, he emphasises that they are so well validated as to leave no credible alternatives. Later in the same book, in the section headed *Alternative Cosmologies*, Professor Peebles is disarmingly frank about dogma in cosmology, and his own role in disseminating it:

> The darker sides to the tradition of dissent in cosmology are the overreactions of those who consider themselves the guardians of the true and canonical faith (as presented in this book), and the tendency for dissent to slip into pathological science. There are documented examples of frivolous criticism of dissenting arguments, which is irrational and destructive.

In one paragraph, here is the message this chapter seeks to convey: We should never, ever allow models to become

---

2 P. J. E. Peebles, *The Principles of Physical Cosmology* (Princeton: Princeton University Press, 1993), 197.

law and dictate the way we do science. If science has a cardinal sin, this is it. Nature and nature alone should direct the course and the method of our enquiry, nothing else. In our methodology, let form be decided by function.

One of the most crucial requirements of human social behaviour is communication. Effective communication between creatures with structured language demands a minimum of disparity between what is meant and what is understood. This offers us something interesting to consider. In the fields of scientific discovery, we have a wonderful method intended to close the communication gap. Each field develops its own terminology — jargon, if you like — which protagonists in that field learn and understand implicitly. Meanings are honed and focussed far more sharply than in general usage, and consequently, when I say "acceleration", most physicists would know precisely what I mean, where non-physicists might default to the common meaning and lose the plot. Jargon is a double-edged sword; the terminology connects me with precision to my fellow physicists, but amongst readers generally, it excludes far more than it includes. In writing this book, I have tried to avoid jargon-rich statements, in the hope that my message can potentially reach a far wider audience.

However, like the unfortunate engineer in Shakespeare's *Hamlet*, it seems I may be hoist with my own petard. Two things happen when one talks science in conversational language: Firstly, one loses the precise transfer of knowledge inherent to specialised terminology, and, secondly, the work is not taken seriously by experts. It's a dichotomy. But I'm sticking with the simpler approach, and I hope that serious scholars will be broad minded enough to come along for the ride.

In the field of physical science, efforts to find a common language with zero scope for misinterpretation led to the adoption of mathematics as the *lingua franca*. It was a system that worked beautifully for centuries, and for the most part works beautifully still. Unrelenting atheist and father of quantum mechanics Paul Dirac tried to use words that you and I could relate to, but of course he was speaking from the point of view of a metamathematician:

> It seems to be one of the fundamental features of nature that fundamental physical laws are described in terms of a mathematical theory of great beauty and power, needing quite a high standard of mathematics for one to understand it. You may wonder: Why is nature constructed along these lines? One can only answer that our present knowledge seems to show that nature is so constructed. We simply have to accept it. One could perhaps describe the situation by saying that God is a mathematician of a very high order, and He used very advanced mathematics in constructing the universe. Our feeble attempts at mathematics enable us to understand a bit of the universe, and as we proceed to develop higher and higher mathematics we can hope to understand the universe better.[3]

---

3 Paul Dirac, "The Evolution of the Physicist's Picture of Nature", *Scientific American* (May 1963).

Clearly, there's a problem. From a technique designed to facilitate the calculation and expression of measurements, mathematics has evolved surreptitiously to a way of obtaining deeper understanding than anything else, and eventually became a way of describing a universe that it first had the exclusive privilege of being able to define. It evolved from a quantitative technique to an all-encompassing qualitative language. Right there, in my opinion, is where it fell from grace.

In the early part of the nineteenth century, mathematicians discovered a free pass: By manipulating terms in their equations, they could free themselves from the constraints of external reality. The world became their metaphorical oyster. Mathematics was transformed, and so were mathematicians. I would have thought that the dangers of finding intense philosophical meaning in glorified arithmetic are obvious, but it seems I was mistaken. The universe became in science's mind little more than shadowy illusions wrapped around a vast set of differential equations. And *still* they cannot agree.

When individuals are trained to high expertise in a manner of expression (whether it is natural language, computer programmes, or mathematics), it sets them apart from ordinary people, and a sense of elitism is sure to follow. What's more, we find that masters of arcane language are unashamedly biased towards it; they seem to enjoy the exclusivity.

Mathematics is perfect dogma.

The philosophy of science ventured by Karl Popper and Thomas Kuhn reveals an alarming truism — science advances only by being challenged. The progressive scientist must search contrary evidence for empirical and logical reasonableness, and ask himself the question, *"Could this explanation apply in the real world?"* If the answer is yes, he needs to weigh it carefully and as objectively as possible against prevailing theory, even if he himself is the author of the accepted view being challenged. Now, let's not bluff ourselves; you and I are surely grown up enough to realise that what we are talking about requires an extremely unlikely purity of mind in the quagmire of human nature.

Consequently, I started to look at science as a sociological phenomenon. Historically, the practice of science has generally followed a path — it's a well-established trend — on which new ideas are consolidated into dogma, politicised, canonised, and protected. Having established that, I turned my attention to the appalling state of affairs that currently prevails. How could it be, I asked myself, that apparently rational women and (mostly) men could spawn and nurture dogma that is so profoundly nonsensical? That brings us to the thorny issues of metaphysics and the paranormal.

There is unavoidable reference to the supernatural in this book, and it is invariably characterised as something undesirable in science. We should talk about this before we go on. I find it's a term that produces confused and imperfectly conceptualised responses more often than not, so let's try to get some clarity on the issue. We can understand and explain only those things that are rational parts of the natural environment in which we live, and that are subject to laws of nature as revealed so far. Of course, there is a vast realm of phenomena which fades out of contention for our specific analysis for various reasons, usually because it is composed of objects that are difficult to see and manipulate empirically. It becomes increasingly difficult to get a clear observational grasp of things as they become more remote, on both the macro and micro scales. Sometimes, we even have to infer the existence of things we have never seen.

If there is any one aspect of the empirical scientific process that above all others requires us to be exceedingly cautious, it is this: Models created to incorporate invisible objects into the body of science should remain strictly hypothetical until they are thoroughly and unambiguously tested against a more reachable natural environment. One example of success in this regard is the Bohr model of the atom. Atoms are too small to be seen individually[4], but the model used in physics and chemistry is without exception aligned with experimental and procedural results in chemistry, and has been used to make many very specific predictions which have been realised in practice. Although it remains just a model to this day, and despite the fact that it contains some serious logical flaws, the atomic model works reliably in experiments, and fits in perfectly with the rules governing the observed structure of matter. For the purposes of science, that is sufficient.

> If we are honest — and scientists have to be — we must admit that religion is a jumble of false assertions, with

---

4 As this book was being submitted to the publishers, Aneta Stodolna of the FOM Institute for Atomic and Molecular Physics (AMOLF) in the Netherlands published in *Physical Review Letters* the first-ever photograph of the orbital structure of a hydrogen atom. She used the latest iteration of a quantum microscope to acquire an image that validated Bohr's model. The technique she used has not yet been verified to my satisfaction.

no basis in reality. The very idea of God is a product
of the human imagination. It is quite understand-
able why primitive people, who were so much more
exposed to the overpowering forces of nature than we
are today, should have personified these forces in fear
and trembling. But nowadays, when we understand
so many natural processes, we have no need for such
solutions.

Paul Dirac[5]

Science is an ongoing process, and much always remains
to be done. The unexplained phenomena are where we
cast our net. This is not supernatural. It is unexplained natural systems. To reiterate, there are many well-observed
phenomena that science cannot yet adequately explain.
That's not the problem that concerns me here. The problem is people who claim knowledge and understanding
of otherworldly phenomena, as well as purported supernatural experiences based upon the supposition of physics
not derived from empirical process. In simple terms, the
problem is validating propositions by nothing more than
superstition.

I try to avoid any connection to concepts my dad called
hocus-pocus. Physics deals with the interactions of material
phenomena. Supernatural explanations should be strictly
taboo, and in my book, they are. That does not mean that
we can see or manipulate everything that has an influence.
On the contrary, as much of physics is invisible as can be

---

5 Quoted in Werner Heisenberg, *Physics and Beyond: Encounters and
Conversations* (New York: Harper & Row, 1971), 85–86.

seen. We cannot *see* force fields, yet they swing planets around the Sun; we cannot *see* atoms, yet we are able to play with their component parts.

Whilst many of the details lie teasingly beyond the grasp of our microscopes and our telescopes, we can nevertheless impute those details because of their interaction with visible objects. A classic contemporary example of this sort of science is the identification of exoplanets. Satellites around stars other than the Sun are too small, too far, and just too dull to be seen directly, yet astronomers have found more than a thousand of these elusive objects. How? By monitoring and measuring minute changes in the properties of stars brought about by the orbiting planet. We can't see them, but we know for sure they are there.

These invisible things are not at all hocus-pocus, they are simply not well lit. Thus, we have dark matter in galaxies: ordinary material structures that cannot yet be observed purely because they are obscured on our line of sight or radiate too weakly to be picked up.

That sort of dark matter is perfectly acceptable to physics. What is *not*, however, is Dark Matter, the supernatural element introduced mathematically to orthodox cosmology in order to get their books to balance. So, to keep our noses clean, we need to be eternally vigilant, and discriminate strongly between dark matter and Dark Matter. That means avoiding like the plague any slightest hint of supernatural terms in our equations. If it is supernatural, science has no business with it.

Paranormal phenomena are best explained as illusions, and illusions can result from a wide variety of circumstances. In astronomy, where we deal with things on a vastly bigger scale than our familiar terrestrial environment, illusions are often simply the consequence of mixed frames of reference. It's an aspect of space science that verges on the arcane mayhem of relativity theory, but we can easily see it for ourselves. There is a particular group of disaffected individuals that puts forward the proposition that geocentrism (the Earth stationary and all else moving about it) is the correct view after all. The Earth, they say, does not orbit the Sun. They regress all the way to Ptolemy's epicycles in a heroic but ultimately foolish attempt to flat-earth the rest of us into buying their scheme. They provide internally consistent mathematics, and all their equations are clean and clear, with good syntax. So why don't I accept what they apparently believe to be true?

Their error is similar to the one that fooled Einstein in believing his own theory. In the case of the neo-geocentrists, they do their geometry with axes anchored on the Earth as a rest frame. If they took one step up, and used the Sun and local stars as the static background, reality would snap into place and their illusion would disappear. This is an important lesson, and it reminded me of the crucial importance of reference frames in understanding relative motion, and the fallacy of taking internal consistency in mathematics as proof of a theory of material reality.[6]

---

6 Dr Einstein's error (detailed in chapter eleven of *The Virtue of Heresy*) also involved the misuse of inertial rest frames. He would use more than one frame of reference in a single analogy or thought experiment, and by that sophistry sought to show that absolute simultaneity does not exist. His experiments (for example, the lightning strikes and the moving train) fail completely if the motion being studied is seen against a single rest frame.

If the Lord Almighty had consulted me before embarking upon his creation, I should have recommended something simpler.

Alfonso X of Castile, referring to the complexity of Ptolemaic model, cited in the preface of John Esten Keller's Alfonso X, El Sabio (1967)

Physics has been in crisis for a century or more due to the invasion of the field by absurd geometry and arcane algebra. Matter has only three dimensions: length, width, and height. Good physics is the study of three-dimensional matter in motion; it involves the observation and analysis of creatures in our environment as they interact with one another in a common rest frame, and includes inferences about causes not yet revealed by observation as long as they are alluded to experimentally.

Good mathematics on the other hand, according to the magi, involves unlimited dimensions, utilizing just one dimension, two dimensions, four dimensions, or as many dimensions as can be imagined, and such conceptual absurdities as incorporating infinity as a term in equations, and dividing by zero. String theory typifies this nonsensical intrusion into physics. String theory may be an amusing diversion for the manipulators of symbols, but it is patently bad physics. It has yet to produce a single thing useful in the real world. String theory, after so much effort by so many vastly talented people for more than thirty years, has not even developed an innovative mathematical technique.

Using mathematics to define reality as part of scientific exploration is akin to homicide detectives turning in desperation to psychics to solve perplexing murders. The psychic may from time to time actually produce a useful clue, ostensibly through communicating with supernatural intelligence, but the odd hit is fished from a sea of misses. The psychic's sly guesswork more often than not becomes a misleading diversion from reality, and objective studies of their output clearly reveal the fraud. There just has to be a better way of doing science.

> Since I have introduced this term [the mathematical cosmological constant] I had always a bad conscience. […] I cannot help to feel it strongly and I am unable to believe that such an ugly thing should be realized in nature.
>
> *Albert Einstein, in a letter to Lemaître, 1947*

In assessing beliefs for verity, we need to be strict: The truthfulness or otherwise of a theory is in no way dependent on your or my ability to present a viable alternative model. Let us be clear on that. One of the most damning obstacles to progress in human thought is our incorrigible trait of not loosening our grip on a belief until a replacement has been thoroughly invested. It may be the hardest thing we ever have to say after "I'm sorry" but there's an important place in our quest for true knowledge for "I do not know."

> The truth may be puzzling. It may take some work to grapple with. It may be counterintuitive. It may contradict deeply held prejudices. It may not be consonant with what we desperately want to be true. But our preferences do not determine what's true.
>
> *Carl Sagan*

Scientists are above all human beings, with all the foibles and limitations that our species generally expresses. Scientists are neither superhuman nor divinely privileged. Scientists, let me tell you right now, are simply plodding bricklayers in the wall of knowledge. They are, as a group, also devilishly impatient, to such an extent that they came before long to deeply envy theologists their ability to gain an understanding of the entire cosmos in just a few pages of the official text by a single, overarching authority.

But let me add also that for all their human-ness, they have devised the only credible way to obtain starkly real, directly testable information about the world of nature. That they have since largely abandoned the empirical scientific method as a credible root for philosophy is simply testimony to their unbridled impatience. Scientists wanted to play God, and by Jiminy, they've done it. The Higgs boson is not the last time they'll refer to one of their solutions as being related to a superbeing with whom they have ostensibly engineered a cosy line of communication. Well, I've had just about *enough* of pompous science. Take a deep breath. Hang onto your socks. The next few paragraphs are going to suggest some additional ground rules for our discussion.

The English word *science* is a derivative of the Latin root *scientia*, which simply means knowledge. In its purest form, science is no more elaborate than a quest for knowledge. Knowledge of what, you may ask? Obviously, knowledge of anything at all, but it implies a search for truth. We would be foolish in science to seek knowledge that is intrinsically *un*true. Science and truth are inextricably intertwined, and I shall be saying a lot more about this partnership as we go

on. For the purposes of this study, we should take the word
science to mean *physical science*, a distinction that is crucial to the arguments of this book.

Science is a study of nature, and therefore eschews
the supernatural. Science is the analysis of real things,
automatically excluding imagined constructs. Imagination plays an unquestionably vital role in every sphere of
human endeavour, but it must necessarily lead to something real before it becomes a candidate for the scrutiny of
science. As long as it remains isolated in the imagination, it
will not be a real thing, but would nevertheless be fruitful
grounds for research in the fields of philosophy, psychology,
theology, and the like. Those fields of enquiry, as important
as they may be, are in their essence not physical science as
we define it here, and my hope therefore is that my readers
display intellectual fortitude sufficient to leave those philosophical discussions out of play until after this book is done,
and we decide whether or not my case has merit.

Belief is far too often created in the minds of man by no
more than being dazzled by perceived authority. I shud-
der when I hear the common justification "but a person of
his standing wouldn't lie about something like this, would
he?" Oh yes he would! He may not be, of course, but the
possibility exists that the promotion of opinions will be
accompanied by falsehoods. In fact, in the whole saga of
belief's infection of human opinion, we will find more
falsehood than truthful integrity, by a significant margin.
We need to come to grips with that. We have a duty to be
sceptical.

One particular part of scientific practice presents itself
as unimpeachable authority, and that is experimental

evidence. It is one of the most prevalent red herrings in all of science. We so easily succumb to the persuasiveness of published experimental results that we are left helpless. It is an enormous problem, and I'm at a loss to suggest a solution. I suppose the scientific community ought to address it through internal self-regulation, but that just won't happen if it is left up to the promoters of the discovery being promoted. The merchants selling belief seem to leave their ethics at home. Thus we have the well-publicised cases of desktop cold nuclear fusion and the car that could run on water and save the planet. Both were supported by well-choreographed experimental results, and both were later shown to be blatant scams. But the cancer roots itself far more deeply than the performances of con artists.

There are two fields of scientific enquiry that stand head and shoulders above the rest when it comes to questionable experimental results — neuroscience and particle physics. So convincing is the propaganda that accompanies the activities of these undoubtedly sincere individuals that we simply fail to ask the relevant questions. And when we do summon the courage to question their methods, they retreat behind a wall of elitist authority.

The "discovery" of the Higgs boson (known colloquially as the "God particle"), for example, required considerable time and incalculable ergs of analysis before the pilots of the accelerator could reach the conclusion that they had seen anything meaningful at all, and still more time and more analysis to reach some measure of consensus that they had in fact seen the debris of the Higgs boson. You see, the Higgs boson is actually invisible. An observer would have to infer its existence from the abstract arrangements of streaks on a photographic plate exposed in an intense magnetic field.

The scientific method requires that any experiment be repeatable, and that testing of experimental results be obtained independently. That means the experiment must be duplicated by the experimenter's peers, in their own laboratory, with replicated equipment. For some modern physics experiments, this becomes in a practical sense impossible. How on Earth does one test the Higgs boson experiment independently of the original equipment and its operators? Raising another ten billion dollars so that Ratcliffe can build a Large Hadron Collider in South Africa to validate discovery of the God particle is simply out of the question.

The problem of independent testability is exacerbated by the fact that only particle physicists can understand and manipulate particle physics. Even if we were able to duplicate the experiment in another, similar collider, we are still stymied. The only people able to read the data so that a coherent result emerges from the particle event are members of that particular church. Only they can talk in tongues, so we just have to take their word for it. The data obtained in the experiment *must* be interpreted in terms of the standard model of particle physics; without the doctrine of a standard model, the results are meaningless. In other words, both the experiment and the preferred interpretation are proof against independent testing, and thus fail to meet the requirements of the scientific method. You and I, my friends, have absolutely no chance of verifying either the experimental procedures or the way conclusions were drawn from the results. To do that, we would have to drill down into the standard model of particle physics, and — heaven forbid — into the hallowed ground of no less than quantum mechanics itself. As a suitably trained mathematician and physicist, I can tell you after a lifetime spent chipping away at standard models, our chances of success are remote. The castle walls of quantum physics are simply too stout for our meagre petard, and we would in all likelihood hurt ourselves more than the standard model we seek to illuminate. It is, in words given to me by Professor Paul Jackson, "impossible, as in trying to strike a match on a wet bar of soap."

So we accept the authority and privileged insight of these men and women, and add their results to our library of belief. Is it belief? Yes it is. We did not come to these convictions by rational thought and logic. We came to them merely by dumb acceptance of their authority. We believe in the people, so we believe what they tell us. Somewhere along the line we have quite forgotten that they too are human beings, with all that it implies.

In this way, we get Brobdingnagian models of cosmological black holes in breathtaking 3D, although we have never seen one; we have thousands of pages in the literature describing in intricate detail the behaviour and structure of neutron stars, yet the only observational sign we can attribute to their existence is a particular spectral signature from a point source of light, and we have vivid, up-close-and-personal descriptions of an unseen God, often with a given name, gender, appearance, and comprehensive personality traits, that far exceed the kind of detail we get from even the most fastidious of crime witnesses in the real

world. It is as if we have observed these things at spectacular resolution far exceeding the power of our instruments,
yet we have not. Do you get the common thread in these
three examples? When we really *want* to believe in something, we happily let our imaginations paint in the details.

Some years ago, certain of my elders in science started
to light a candle in my idea train — I heard them say, first
to each other, and later to me personally, that the crisis *in*
science is not *of* science. The turgid maelstrom that has
brought to its knees the classical scientific method, whereby
the fundamentals of science are associated in a way that
produces new fundamentals and new progress, has nought
to do with the tools of science. Our telescopes are good, better than ever in fact. The machines in our laboratories are
outstanding. We are equipped as never before to make real
progress, but we do not, at least not in fundamental physics.
No, the barrier to uncovering the foundational principles of
physics is psychosocial, not physical. The only real progress
currently being made in the field is being achieved by engineers, using principles that are at least one hundred years
old. Theoretical physics is an exercise in anarchy. Mankind
is drunk on the glory of its own ideas.

The late visionary cosmologist Carl Sagan once uttered
these inspiring words:

> In science, it often happens that scientists say, 'You
> know, that's a really good argument; my position
> is mistaken.' And then they actually change their
> minds and you never hear that old view from them
> again. They really do it. It doesn't happen as often as
> it should, because scientists are human and change is

sometimes painful, but it happens every day. I cannot recall the last time something like that happened in politics or religion.

Tragically, science is succumbing to politics and religion too, and the objectivity that Sagan is referring to is withering. But I remain steadfast that empirical science is our only hope of developing a worldly knowledge-base free of self-promotion and the suffocating effect of belief. Perhaps someone ought to write a book about it....

No matter how glowingly scientists describe the virtues of the scientific method, it is and always shall be a human system operated by people. Whether science is in practice self correcting will depend upon that unavoidable human factor, and can succeed only inasmuch as the mindset of the person in the driving seat will allow it to. The scientific method is an ideal, something to aim at, and make no mistake: it's a very good one.

The classical scientific method is greatly misunderstood, even by scientists. It is central to the way that the scientific knowledge base is built and maintained, so it would be sensible to discuss the scientific method in some detail. The origins of rational analysis of our natural environment were found in the darkness of antiquity. The earliest recorded accounts suggest that the motivation for an objective methodology was born out of philosophical protest at being tied to prevailing superstitions and theological metaphysics of the day.

For millennia, intellectual development occurred almost exclusively in the cloisters of priesthood; literacy was the privilege of an elite minority, usually the officers of religious oligarchies. In ancient Egypt, in the Mayan civilisation, in the Israel of Jesus, amongst the tribes of Europe, and in the Babylonian, Indian, and Far Eastern dynasties, all formal learning was in the hands of priests, and they wrote the records of history without even a hint of independent peer review. Missionaries of the Church formed the advance guard of colonial imperialism. History was recorded through the eyes of a politically entrenched religious doctrine. It amounts to a closed, self-promulgating loop, duplicated in every learned culture in antiquity without regard to geographical location.

Consequently, all learning was suffused in superstition and religious doctrine. Astronomers particularly suffered this restriction on their acquisition of knowledge, and no ancient astronomical artefact shows signs of being free of theological considerations of some kind. The huge monuments that emerged in antiquity — the pyramids of Egypt, Central America, and Asia; Stonehenge in England; and Newgrange in Ireland, to name a few — all had astronomical alignments, and equally importantly, represented the architecture of religious practice in that era. Astronomers in the courts of Europe were forced, on pain of death, to practice astrology. There was sure to come a time when scholars would want to free themselves of the yoke of supernatural spectres, but it was a long time coming.

The scientific method offers a comprehensive technique for analysing phenomena in the natural world, extracting measured data from those phenomena, formulating new knowledge related to those data, and thereby correcting or integrating previous understanding. The knowledge thus obtained comes exclusively from empirical evidence, subject to the principles of reasoned analysis. The crux that distinguishes scientific enquiry from less rigorous methods is this: Scientists subject themselves to a discipline that lets reality speak for itself. It is precisely here that the scientific method stumbles in its tracks; the required purity is far harder to achieve than one might think.

A concise précis of the process adhered to by scientists is as follows:

- Firstly, observation. Something in nature is seen to require explanation or simplification to a set of principles that help to interpret the bigger picture;
- the problem to be solved is delineated, and usually takes the form of a question at the head of a blank page;
- then, prior validated evidence related to this question is obtained and held in reference;
- a hypothesis is derived from both existing evidence and the formulation of the question (with the critical caveat that the hypothesis must in principle be falsifiable);
- a set of unambiguous, clearly stated predictions representing the logical consequences of the hypothesis is delineated;
- the hypothesis is empirically tested against reality, and measured data are obtained;

- analysis of those data seeks to falsify the
  hypothesis as per the guidelines set out by
  Karl Popper[7]; and finally
- the hypothesis is either embraced as a theory
  or a law, or it is modified and retested, or it
  is rejected outright.

The ultimate test of the proposal is twofold: Carefully observing whether it works consistently and without exception in the real world, and checking for ambiguity.

Critical analysis of the model is absolutely independent of any alternative model or replacement theory.

It's the testing at every step of the way that's crucial; it's the challenge of reality that ultimately separates the sheep from the goats. In the background as I write, the television relays a cricket match between South Africa and Pakistan. It struck me that I was being given a wonderfully appropriate analogy for the point I'm making: Cricket is a game of strategy, and armchair critics are in no short supply. The commentary is performed by a pair of knowledgeable

---

7 Karl Popper (1902–1994) CH FBA FRS was an Austrian-British philosopher and professor at the London School of Economics. Popper is best known as the father of the principle of falsifiability. He is generally regarded as one of the greatest philosophers of science of the twentieth century. Popper is known for his rejection of the classical inductivist views on the scientific method, in favour of empirical falsification: A theory in the empirical sciences can never be proven, but it can be falsified, meaning that it can and should be scrutinised by decisive experiments. If the outcome of an experiment contradicts the theory, one should refrain from ad hoc manoeuvres that evade the contradiction merely by making it less falsifiable. Popper is also known for his opposition to the classical justificationist account of knowledge which he replaced with critical rationalism (courtesy of Wikipedia).

authorities on the game, in this case both retired national cricketers. One of them is renowned former South African cricket captain and first-class batsman, Kepler Wessels. The captain of the day decides on his team's game plan. The commentators weigh in with their own competing strategies, and give their reasons on air for the improvements they suggest. They are convincing, I must say, and make powerful argument for their ideas. However, of the three competing strategies — one each for the commentators, and the plan being executed on the field by the playing captain — only one is being tested against reality. We'll never know how good the commentators' hypotheses were, because as compelling as they might make their case in the commentary box, it is never tested on the field of play.

Sir Fred Hoyle, one of young Stephen Hawking's professors at Cambridge and amongst his sternest critics, was co-author of the once-popular steady state theory in cosmology. Big Bang theory usurped steady state's throne in the 1950s, much to Hoyle's obvious chagrin. Hoyle, one of the most accomplished theoretical astrophysicists of the twentieth century, appeared unable to comprehend that the criticisms he levelled at Big Bang applied equally to his own model of the universe.

> On scientific grounds this big bang assumption is much less the palatable of the two. For it is an irrational process that cannot be described in scientific terms. [...] On philosophical grounds too I cannot see any good reason for preferring the big bang idea. Indeed it seems to me in the philosophical sense to

be a distinctly unsatisfactory notion, since it puts the basic assumption out of sight where it can never be challenged by a direct appeal to observation.

Sir Fred Hoyle, in his book
The Nature of the Universe, 1950.

Scientific knowledge and the rules that govern it are inextricably bound to empirical evidence. The empirical scientific method begins and ends with observation. It is always and forever subject to falsification as the knowledge base expands almost exponentially with new discoveries. It is therefore hardwired into the method that no theory can be held with complete certainty, and by implication, that it does not allow sacred cows in any shape, size, or form. The *method* employed by scientists does indeed have built-in self-correcting mechanisms, and by design acknowledges any anomalies that might arise. Sadly, scientists themselves are not nearly so magnanimous or scrupulously honest.

You know, in cosmology it seems we allow ourselves the freedom to propose just about anything. Nothing is too preposterous when it comes to explaining the universe as a whole. Why this should be so, and why it particularly affects universal modelling are quandaries for which I am grateful, for it is precisely these questions that brought me to the present book. In *The Virtue of Heresy* I coined the term *spatial credibility factor*[8], which was at the time a somewhat naive expression of the notion that uncertainty is proportional to remoteness:

---

8 Spatial credibility factor: an uncertainty brought about by remoteness; the degree to which distance decreases our ability to resolve detail.

"The further away things are, the less we tend to believe them. The corollary to this theorem is 'The further removed we are from any phenomenon, the greater is our licence and latitude in describing it.'"[9]

The contemplation of very remote things leads us inevitably to a place where we should include awareness of the role of irrelevancies in building a background world view — the metaphorical laboratory bench if you will — to our endeavours in the field of physical science. In Isaac Newton's day, the heading "physics" had not yet been inscribed upon the parchment of scientific enquiry; it was called natural philosophy, and that explains a lot.

Nature was then and always shall be I suppose a very great and tantalising mystery, and we quite understandably indulged our faculty for placing the cart before the horse: We have allowed our philosophical musings to become the suggested cause in natural events, and empirical evidence merely the effect. I propose that placing subjective opinion over objective data is precisely where we go wrong. In that scheme, our beliefs determine reality, and that is doing things quite the wrong way around.

A further application of the spatial credibility factor has grave implications for the matter being considered in the present work: the *hypo-stack*. I contrived the term to describe a commonly found structural design of scientific models. Hypo-stacks are quite literally a stack of untested, interdependent hypotheses, hence the name.

---

9 Hilton Ratcliffe, *The Virtue of Heresy: Confessions of a Dissident Astronomer* (CreateSpace, 2008).

Models of this class form a theoretical house of cards, without adequate solidity in their foundation to support higher strata. The spatial credibility factor applies here just as pertinently as it does in space and time; as we explore the model further away from its nucleus, the more uncertainty multiplies, and the greater the likelihood of error. In real-world applications, the spatial credibility factor renders hypo-stacks almost useless.

Let's talk about reality checks. The visionary philosopher Bertrand Russell gave us the analogy of an orbiting teapot. Russell's argument was that if he were to claim that a teapot orbits about the Sun somewhere in the chasm of space between the Earth and Mars, it would be ludicrous to expect others to believe him simply on the grounds that they cannot prove him wrong. He was alluding specifically to the burden of proof, and I must agree with him: The burden of proof lies always with the person making unfalsifiable claims, and not with the person he is trying to convince.

It is not up to us to prove him wrong; it is his duty to prove to his peers that his alleged teapot is really doing what he claims it is. He remains guilty until proven innocent, as it were. Until such verification is forthcoming, his assertions ought to be excluded from the realm of physical science and find support only amongst those who want to believe.

Arguably, the most effective guideline in establishing objectivity at the commencement of a scientific adventure came via the pen of Sherlock Holmes author Sir Arthur Conan Doyle. Doyle's principle of impossibility (if I may call it that) states that in any investigation, first remove from the evidence that which is impossible; the solution will lie in what remains.

This in no way implies that what today seems impossible might not on a brighter morrow be quite feasible; we can proceed only on the strength of our current understanding. Tomorrow, if we are shown to have been ignorant and misguided, we should be brave enough to recant. We can never be completely certain, but that does not grant us licence to be reckless with our investigation.

The root of the problem with contemporary scientific practice is that it is predominantly model dependent. A model is a simulation of nature, relying on *if-then-else* logic strings to build a vision of what nature may be like, *if* the assumptions of the model and the relationships between them are indeed correct. A model is an imaginary solution to a given set of questions.

Our ability to create spectacularly impressive models has improved exponentially with advances in computing power and sophistication of the programmes that run them. Contemporary scientific models incorporate a vast range of base data, display them in visually dazzling ways, and in my view, resemble Hollywood movies more than sober physics. Models are in actuality no more than metaphors for nature; we are too easily seduced into believing that they *are* reality, and represent truth more accurately than does truth itself.

An analogy is at best mere proxy for the truth, and should be seen as no more than an illustration to clarify the arguments being presented. Analogies are not themselves part of those arguments. Because theoretical models are little more than imaginative metaphors, the advent of model-dependent physics (science-by-analogy) in the first half of the twentieth century has had a profound effect on the way things get done, and on the outcomes achieved.

The practise of model-dependent physics unfolds something like this: a model gets presented to the world and its proponents lobby for support. They seek support not so much from scientists in the field, but from society in general, and that means promoting the model becomes a sociopolitical issue. Potential sponsors most often cannot judge the proposed hypothesis by understanding the underlying physics, but almost entirely through the subjective appeal of the author's propaganda. The debate sways on the conceptual seductiveness of the model and not on the science it purports to represent. We wind up arguing about the metaphor rather than the facts, and we ought to know by now how bad that is for a truthful outcome. It's like trying to drive your car by arguing about the rules of the road.

The presentation of models to the public via the media, and subsequent transformation of a supposedly scientific analysis into a political cause follows a well-established pattern. In fact, it has become something of an industry. Nothing ensures the success of a model in the marketplace more than that it provides an opportunity for revenue. If people, groups, or governments can make money out of it, it will gather momentum with velocity astonishingly disproportionate to its factual base.

The effectiveness of democratic governance depends critically upon the vibrancy of opposition. If no effective opposition exists in parliament, government tends towards virtual dictatorship even if members were democratically elected in the first place. There is no doubt that science too is governed. There are rules, and the rules are enforced by consensus among self-appointed elite. An example is the interestingly named "concordance model" in cosmology, which was entrenched at the outset by no more than complicit agreement amongst the most influential of the elders crusading for general relativity theory. The publication of empirical results is overtly biased towards the prevailing theoretical models, and the acceptance or rejection of material for the most-cited journals is determined more by editorial policy than by the scientific integrity of candidate material. To create the impression of fairness, censors filter a token amount of criticism into the literature, but it is kept strictly within acceptable policy limits by the peer-review process. The orthodoxy protects itself from heterodox evidence.

Unconstrained by external challenges and the discipline of accountability, people tend to slide down a slippery slope towards megalomania. The only people who really believe in the principle of benevolent dictatorship are the dictators themselves. Once a man — any man — attains a position in society where he has effectively gagged and demoralised dissent, he becomes corrupt. That is as certain as the gravitation that holds you and me to Mother Earth. His self-perceived value seems to increase in direct proportion to his disdain for those who say that he is wrong. This attitude manifests in arrogance, contempt, and plain bad manners, and is often expressed in ad *hominem* attacks on his critics.

One could draw a parallel with metamathematicians. Remove the constraint of external reality and you invite into the psyche a delusional condition where mathematicians consciously or unconsciously become "masters of the universe." All the good work of abstract mathematics is seriously undermined by the psychological instability it induces.

That is not to say that metamathematicians are all raving lunatics — some are, definitely, but many are not. They still walk their dogs, pay their parking tickets, and remember to get dressed in the morning. And sometimes, I am led to believe, they even talk intelligibly. It is their contention that external reality is as they define it that brings them dangerously close to fitting a clinical description of insanity.

It is by now well established that belief leads reasoning and not the other way around[10], so the question naturally follows — what causes belief? I spent some considerable time, commencing in my undergraduate years, believing in Big Bang theory. My gut feel is that my personal belief in the standard cosmological model of the day, albeit impermanent, may hold some valuable clues to the nature of the beast.

I *thought* I came to believe in Big Bang theory with good reason; but I did not. I learned that Edwin Hubble had discovered a relationship between redshift[11] and

---

10 Michael Shermer, *The Believing Brain* (New York: Times Books, 2011); Jesse Bering, *The Belief Instinct* (New York: W.W. Norton & Co., 2011).

11 Redshift: We shall be coming across the term *redshift* frequently in any tale of the cosmos, so let me explain for those readers who may not be familiar with what it means. Redshift is a spectral signature commonly used in astrophysics, often invoked to indicate relative motion and, by implication, distance. A higher redshift object should be appreciably further away than one with lower redshift. Red and blue are colours at opposite ends of the light spectrum. Red light has a longer wavelength than blue, so a light source moving *away* from the observer would have

distance; but he had not. I was taught that Penzias and Wilson had found surrounding radiation that exactly matched the predictions of the standard model of cosmology; but that too was incorrect.

I was persuaded, without a single, good, verifiable reason, to *believe*.

I propose that we are not looking at the universe as it *is*; what it actually is remains unseen and it's that pristine state which we seek, in an ongoing process. Our objective is not complete understanding, or anything near it. It is simply to add to what we have learnt so far. It's not the fundamental, overarching nature of existence; it is merely the simple relationships we have managed to rationalise from our surroundings. We start here and proceed outward. We cannot know the meaning of life. We can't see the whole picture, and must remain satisfied with husbanding our little piece of it by logic and direct experience so that it grows with each passing generation.

I refer once again to the first principles of scientific enquiry: In an infinite universe, we will always be

---

its light waves stretched and thus spectral lines would be shifted towards the red end of the spectrum. That's redshift. The degree of shift or deflection in the lines is obtained by comparison to a benchmark taken to be the positions they occupy in local light, that is, sunlight. A source coming *towards* us would have its waves compressed, and spectral lines would be moved towards the blue (blueshift). Most celestial light sources are said to be moving away from the Earth, so the buzzword is *redshift*. The stretching or compression of a waveform signal because of the relative motion of the observer and the source of the signal is called the Doppler effect, and is readily appreciated in sound waves — when a motor car, for example, passes a stationary observer by the roadside, he hears the pitch of the sound drop as it moves away from him. That's the Doppler effect, and it causes redshift in light from a source that's receding from us.

significantly more ignorant than we are wise. We search for knowledge as informed approximations of the true nature of our world. It takes place by exploring that which is unknown, whilst always challenging and testing the knowledge that was revealed by the pioneers that went before us. So, if we can't see the world as it is, how should we best attempt to unravel its secrets?

Without delving into all the reasons that support my view and the nuances of the method that emerges from it, I maintain that our field of enquiry is best looked at as a machine, that is, as a system producing tangible results, interconnected along all dimensions as strict cause-and-effect interactions, and progressing along the axis of time. The implication of this world view is that we explain only the reality of our mutual experience. I cannot see atoms; therefore I use an atomic model in order to better understand the things I can see. I don't use the atomic model to explain atoms; I use it to improve my understanding of a teacup.

Fortunately, one of the most virulent breeding grounds for self-supporting theoretical conjectures is the field of cosmology; fortunately, because there the phenomenon has arguably the least chance of doing us real harm. Theorists can say whatever they like about the mysterious cosmos with virtual impunity. As long as the things they propose are confined to the largest imaginable scales, we are safe, but there is always the very real risk of procedural backwash infecting fields where empirical science tries to produce real-world outcomes. Astronomy, for example, almost by definition an observational science, is already strictly governed by the standard model of cosmology.

Ideas spawned in cosmology, most of them unsubstantiated by independent measurement, are included in undergraduate curricula as basic premises of physics. Thus the dogma is entrenched and reinforced to the extent that emerging physicists find it difficult to appreciate life without it.

Many of the procedural diseases afflicting physical science are without names, because those suffering from the maladies (the ruling class) cannot self-diagnose, and thus feel no need to develop the nomenclature. I am guilty of inventing quite a few, including of course the oft-mentioned *hypo-stack*.

Hypo-stacking refers to a theoretical house of cards, where concepts and conjectures are used as a concrete step up for further theoretical structures. It is actually a manifestation of belief in scientific practice. The question the perpetrators of hypo-stacking have failed to answer to my satisfaction is whether or not the foundational idea of the stack is resilient enough to carry the load. Hypo-stacked models, like Big Bang theory for example, are constantly being massaged to keep them standing.

In my view, the clearest examples of hypo-stacking come from religion. In order to satisfy nagging questions about the origin of the perceived universe, religionists introduce a Dark Matter element that they reverently name God. At that level of understanding, one is hard pressed to find them wrong. It seems fairly obvious to me that some sort of driving, sustaining, and constraining energy field is keeping the cosmos in order on the grand scale, providing the template for local cycles of life and reproduction. Then it goes haywire: From that vague notion of a logically probable dominant energy field, religion constructs an elaborate hypo-stack, and, in an odd kind of way, I feel grateful to them for doing so, because it illustrates my point so clearly.

Rational deduction suggests the likelihood of some form of guiding energy. What religions have created from that is quite incredible. In order to develop the basic idea into a religious doctrine, they canonise the original notion so that it is accepted as an axiom upon which a model may be built. Human beings across the globe developed elaborate sets of ideas based upon the premise of an almighty God that reflects the philosophical or superstitious needs of the societies in which they were spawned.

To return to the hypo-stack: a person seeking to explain the cosmos may quite logically deduce from the meagre facts of cosmology that the universe could not possibly have come about spontaneously, and that it is therefore likely that a supernatural external ultrapower is involved. No one could prove him wrong, and he is perfectly rational in holding the opinion that a higher, intelligent, living energy is at the helm of the existence. I may not share his certainty, but I cannot by either logic or science deny him the right to hold that belief. It's what he does next that leaves me cold. He gives us a detailed, unflinching description of what God looks like, how it behaves, what it expects from us, and how it has interacted with humans on Earth in early history (when God, apparently, was far more generous with miracles and prophets that it is today).

Science *should* be concerned with real outcomes; pure abstraction belongs with art, along with our innate appreciation of the aesthetic, the ability to differentiate harmony and discord, and then, without too great a leap, the instinctive impetus for morality, ethics, and sympathy. Science, in its pure form, operates on the premise that total knowledge is impossible and that discovery is a journey rather than a destination.

Theological philosophy on the other hand insists that the ultimate questions be addressed; hence the unconstrained imagination that produces polymorphous deities visible only to those with the privilege of backstage passes. The crucial point is that the drives to pursue both streams of thought — the exploratory drive that motivates scientific enquiry, and the belief instinct that encourages our amusement with superheroes — are there to some degree in all of us.

The boundaries between belief and knowledge are not always clear. Well-known media astronomer Neil deGrasse Tyson once said, *"The good thing about science is that it's true whether or not you believe in it."* Perhaps inadvertently, Dr Tyson hit the nerve — what he said is in principle quite true, if only one could rid science of opinions held solely in good faith. But, I fear, one cannot. Belief — in the negative sense — has invaded science in recent times and overtly made its presence felt. If I am correct in my thesis, this has always been so. Human beings fall instinctively into opinions that have their origins in belief rather than observation, experiment, and calculation. Our mindset is established at the outset by a pervasive belief instinct, and the observation, experiment, and calculation follow in due course. Those results, in their turn, are coloured to such an extent by pre-existing convictions that the facts seen in the data become no more than subjective artefacts that we contort until they match our beliefs.

In the directionless long-wavelength radiation that hisses through space from all sides, cosmologists found patterns that they interpret as an image of the primordial universe, just moments after the Big Bang. Thus, the microwave background in particular received the adjective *cosmic*, meaning it was somehow primordial, while the other backgrounds were sensibly blamed on celestial structures.

Let us consider a mantra for our meditation: *In the song of the sky, we make out a 3D rendition of our personal God.* An instinctive preset in our cognitive mechanisms means that we can always find signal where there is actually just noise.

And that ties in neatly with our propensity for *belief*.

> *We are just an advanced breed of monkeys on a minor planet of a very average star. But we can understand the universe. That makes us something very special.*
>
> STEPHEN HAWKING

Artist unknown. "Flammarion." Wood engraving in Camille Flammarion's L'atmosphère: Météorologie Populaire. 1888.

In the unforgiving post-graduate world where I was expected to apply my knowledge usefully to the satisfaction of my benefactors, I slowly came to realise that education was really a form of classical conditioning in the Pavlovian mode; we were its dogs, and both the tricks we were to perform and the rewards we would consequently receive were made clear to us all.

4

BELIEF, INSTINCT, BEHAVIOUR

Every dogma has its day

A FRIEND OF MINE told me recently of his miracu-
lous recovery from cancer. He belongs to a fringe religious
group, and assures me that the subsiding of his torment
came as a consequence of his theological zeal. In a manner of speaking, he's right: it does. But contrary to what
my friend likes to tell us, it is not *what* he believes that creates the effect. It's simply that he believes, period. Faith
provides a preferred explanation. Thus it is that Christians
ascribe their recovery to faith in Jesus, Hindus to karma,
Buddhists to right living, atheists to themselves, and Muslims to the grace of Islam. One's belief system determines a
particular, exclusive causal dynamic for conditions that in
actuality strike anyone without prejudice, regardless of the
badge their point of view hides behind.

Although I am convinced that what I propose can
solve or at the very least alleviate some vexing problems

associated with proselytised social opinions and cult-like bonding, getting people on board will be no easy task. There is an historical precedent to this, and my thesis is perhaps unique in that it proposes the law by which it fails itself. I find myself in difficulties with scientific pragmatism somewhat akin to those experienced by the promoters of Marxist socialism-slash-communism. The success or failure of any scheme as a new social paradigm has nothing to do with its correctness. Marxist socialism was widely resisted in spite of all the compelling arguments raised in its support, for one simple reason: It goes against instinct.

To the scientific mind, belief systems are crazy; they revolve around paranormal or extra-normal phenomena. But they also have an internal justification mechanism. On their own terms, they are legitimate, and tend to consider their doctrine an expression of profound wisdom. The "word of God" is a rubber stamp for anything.

There is an inevitable intellectual framework that surrounds the practice of meditation which shows all too clearly the back loop of mind over mindlessness. It would appear that in the cold light of day, spiritual revelation is no more than mental feedback.

What do we know about belief? Quite a lot, actually. By the definition we are using here, belief is a set of opinions *not* derived from, or sustained by, a sequence of logic and rational thought. Belief is distinct from knowledge in how it is derived and sustained, and to a great extent, how it is expressed. If we hold the opinion that the Sun is the nucleus of the Solar System because we interpret a passage in the Bible that way, it is belief; if on the other hand we maintain the very same opinion as a result of geometrical measurement and observation, it is knowledge. If we accept and embrace the validity of general relativity theory simply because we think Albert Einstein is awesome, we express belief; if our support of the model comes from stringent empirical testing, it is knowledge.

I invite you to apply this distinction to a good few standard models that rule the organisation of our thoughts. I would imagine you'd be as surprised and astonished as I was at just how prevalent faith-based convictions are in every facet of human exploratory behaviour, including, to our utter amazement, the sanctimoniously rational canons of science. More often than not, we suffer from the *illusion* of knowledge; we *know*, beyond a shadow of doubt, that what we believe is true. It doesn't matter a jot what the belief is. It's true simply because we believe it so.

One of the trickiest aspects of this field of study is the universality of belief. Early on, I had seen this in discussions on the nature of belief with some devout Christian friends. Although they would agree with me in principle on most of the points I put forward, there was a caveat from which none of them departed: Their *own* belief remained the exception. Whereas they agreed that opposing belief systems invariably misled the believer and removed him from the truth, for them personally, belief had a diametrically opposite effect. It was their personal faith, they assured me very earnestly, that introduced them to the truth and enhanced their appreciation of the world from there on in.

It thus became clear that I would not get to the objective scientific basis of belief unless I could somehow extract myself from the vortex. Like it or not, I had to accept the stark reality: In the search for objective truth, *all* belief is a negative filter — all of it, most especially my own. The scientist can entertain no exceptions to this.

So it was that I happened upon the golden rule of belief science: Avoid at all costs using one's own belief, wholly or partially, in any case study. It's so enticing to do so that we easily fall into the trap, especially because we have privileged insight to our own hearts and minds that no one else could possibly have. I am the only person on Earth who can see my thoughts.[1] But belief is so inextricably tied to our inner sense of well-being that we drown in it. That's why psychotherapists (or any medical professional for that matter) should not treat themselves. Successful analysis depends critically upon the degree of objectivity a third person brings to the table. I like to draw an analogy from astronomy: We can see the neighbouring Andromeda galaxy much more clearly than we can our own Milky Way, even though Andromeda is three million light years away. In terms of our home in the cosmic neighbourhood, we cannot by any means see the forest, only trees.

> There may be fairies at the bottom of the garden. There is no evidence for it, but you can't prove that there aren't any, so shouldn't we be agnostic with respect to fairies?
>
> *Richard Dawkins*

We need to address the crucial difference between *"not believe"* and *"believe not."* Dr Dawkins is technically

---

1 Neuroscientists are making claims that their machines and see and decipher human thought. I don't think they can.

correct, of course, and yes, we should be agnostic with respect to fairies. In my opinion, we should be agnostics, period. Recognition of our own ignorance is the first step in objective analysis. However, the question really is, should we be *active* agnostics about fairies? If we do not apply our faculty for selective discrimination, we shall simply drown under the tsunami of information.

Fairies are not put forward as real creatures by any but a very small band of naive dreamers, so serious discussion and dedicated thought time are not warranted. The matter of religion and the God hypothesis is quite different though, and deserves to be studied, if for no other reason than that it is a widely held sociological trend. There are classes and degrees dedicated to philosophy and religion, and rightly so. My point is that science is another animal, and needs to be studied objectively.

We perceive the environment via the agency of our senses, and this inbound information is interpreted by means of associative logic to create a rational mental picture of the world about us. There are internal reference points providing further input and nuance, for example memory, imagination, and instinct; but most importantly, we should realise that we perceive it all in the steady equilibrium of a frame of reference. Our ability to be rational — that is, to hold a world view that aligns reasonably closely with the objective reality of our surroundings — depends critically upon our grasp of the primary frame of reference that anchors our thinking. If that safe harbour fails us, we succumb to a tempest of insanity wherein we are rudderless. This is a harsh and tragic consequence of losing our frame of reference.

It's important to grasp both the relevance and the essential differences between *logical* and *rational*, because what we're attempting here is a blend of the two. *Logical* may be defined as abiding by strict principles of validity, or showing and following rational thought. *Rational* describes thought sequences based upon reason and logic. It's confusing. They seem at first glance to be synonyms, but they aren't. The crucial difference between logical and rational lies in the terms of reference, or as Albert Einstein preferred to put it, in the *inertial frame*. Logic remains valid regardless of a reference frame, because it consists of an internally secure series of steps. Each stage in the process of logic anchors upon the one preceding it, and in turn anchors the one that follows; it matters not a whit where it is done or which way is up and which is down. Logic is thus an internally referenced system. Rational thought, on the other hand, is externally constrained; the frame in which it performs is critical to the outcome.

Perhaps we can better illustrate the nature of these two concepts with some analogies. Think of a computer programme. The machine code proceeds from one step to the next in a strictly logical way, and the validity of each term as a consequence of what went before is critical to the outcome. If a single step fails, no valid conclusion is possible. That is logic. What's going on in the world outside the computer doesn't affect the validity of the programme sequence. It's internally regulated. Now take a step back for a moment and look at the computer that runs the machine code. We unravel the sense of it by placing it against the backdrop of the known world. It is externally regulated. Rational thought has different priorities from logical thought. It references the real world and a shared sense of reality in order to function properly. Being rational is essentially different. For instance, a madman may believe with internally isolated logic that he's a bumble bee, but referencing the real world he shares with us shows us that he is being irrational. His frame of reference is skew. That's where he goes wrong.

Polarity is an essential element of our frame of reference, and we're born with it. One of our primal fears is that of falling. It's wired in, and our reference is gravitation. We don't need to be taught about the concepts of up and down, or which is which. Gravitation has a direct influence on the way we behave: The poles of up and down are not places, but rather an invariant direction that anchors our common reality. Gravitation forms a dependable, globally accessible axis in our terrestrial frame of reference. The same is true of time. Like the dimension of gravity, time is linear and works in one direction only. People who claim to be able to free themselves from gravity's eternal clutch and float up into the sky, like those who assure us they can time travel and manipulate past and future remotely from the present moment, are nuts. Sorry. They are. Put another way, we could say they've been smoking their socks. They've lost their grip on the real world's reference frame.

The primary polarity in our current study (and we shall be chatting a lot more about polarity before we're through) is *subjective* and *objective*. I have included formal definitions in the glossary at the back of the book, but for something this important, it's worth throwing in a working definition or two here to make sure we're singing from the same hymn sheet. Subjective analysis depends upon and emanates from our feelings and opinions; objective analysis, on the other hand, does not. Objectivity is a view of things as they actually are, whereas subjectivity looks at what we *think* about reality.

Let me illustrate the difference with an everyday example. I am eating alone at a crowded restaurant, and notice two diners, strangers to me, lost in animated conversation at a table on the other side of the room. That's the objective view; it's "out there", more or less the same as anyone else in the room would see. My feeling is that I'm pleased I don't have to share their table because it looks as though I would be intruding on their privacy, and that would make me uncomfortable. That's my subjective view. It's how I feel about the scene I observed objectively. It's internal and personal. Naturally, I need both objectivity and subjectivity to make my way in life, but only objectivity gives me the cold facts. I trust the difference is made sufficiently clear. They are in a sense opposite, both of them necessary, critical aspects of human intellectual exploration.

Where do beliefs come from? Short answer: they come from instinct. I love my girlfriend, and believe the most incredible things about her, because of the instinct to procreate. I defend my home and believe that the burglar is a lethal threat, because of the territorial instinct. I fear walking across a two-foot-wide plank between two rooftops, and believe that it can't be done, because of the instinct for self-preservation. If I didn't love my girlfriend, if I had no home, if the two-foot-wide plank was on my lawn, my beliefs about them would be significantly different.

Let's be very clear here: Instinct changes and controls our thinking far more than we realise, and provides the energy to convert knowledge into belief. Instinct lies at the root of the metamorphosis of data into dogma. Belief is the face we put onto our drive to survive as a species. Belief *is* an instinct.

If we are to understand the phenomenon of belief, grasping the order of priority is crucial. Homo sapiens is predisposed to believe; we come to believe first, then (optionally) employ logic to sustain and promote it. Furthermore, by the time we have matured enough to formulate scientific hypotheses, we have already believed for years. Although science is (or should be) the outcome of rational and systematically logical analysis of the world about us, it has to make its way through a maze of firm convictions before it can expect to be analysed with even a modicum of objectivity. Religious faith, on the other hand, is obtained viscerally, or to use a term from theology, spiritually. It emerges unconnected in any way with scientifically organised thinking, and indeed, in the maturation of humans, belief, driven as it is by instinct, precedes systematic rationale by a significant margin.

However—and this is important—scientific *faith*, although strictly non-theistic, is the product of the very same psychosocial imperatives as secular faith, including the canonisation of authority, metaphysical intrigue, self-gratification and self-importance, a sense of comfort and security in belonging, and so on. The causal stimuli are the same; religious faith and secular faith are two sides of the same coin.

One thing that has emerged from this *Socks* expedition is that it is our ownership of a particular set of beliefs that sets it above competing paradigms, irrespective of any other intellectual considerations. Religion is the political expression of theology, and as such, is defined by the tribal and cultural flavour of the place and time in which it emerges. The concepts of sin and God and moral behaviour have their roots in a deep, instinctual reservoir in each of us, but the specific expression of those things is constrained by tribal cultural traditions, and varies considerably from tribe to tribe, place to place, and culture to culture. For instance, what is moral to the broad Christian consensus is often severely at odds with what is morally correct in Islam.

Morality and the sense of right and wrong change over time as cultures evolve (consider animal sacrifice, for example), but each religion remains locked into the essential historical and sociological roots from whence it came. Thus, Christians still use the Bible as their scriptural reference, although it has in many ways been left behind by evolving Christian morality. This culture-lock detracts from the essential truth of any religion, and with respect I reiterate that the efforts of Christian apologists reduce the essential purity of unadorned faith. In principle, it should be possible to practice Christianity (if it is indeed theological truth) without any reference at all to the Bible or any other intellectual argument.

If a particular mindset is derived from instinct, it is resistant to rational thought. When we feel the emotional hurt of romantic rejection, we can't simply rationalise it away. It would be wonderful if we could quickly and efficiently heal ourselves of that sort of distress by intellectual argument, but we cannot. All the empathy and good advice in the world doesn't suddenly fix the situation and restore us to sanity; we continue to hurt and hold patently irrational views of the situation. The instinctive persona operates by its own rules, and we only very slowly come to our senses and feel whole again.

A broken heart is one of the most devastating distortions of reality a human being can feel, and it is quite impervious to logic. Instinct trumps common sense any day of the week. Later, when we have healed, we may well shake our heads in embarrassment at just how crazy we were, but at the time we would have nothing of it. There is a profound lesson in this for us, but it's a bitter pill to swallow. Belief makes us nuts. It really does.

This is worth repeating: Belief is a conviction held independently of rational discourse. In fact, belief or faith is held by a broad cross-section of believers to be superior to intellectual analysis and in their minds dominates it. What is not generally recognised is that belief is not the exclusive province of religion; far from it. In scientific parlance, beliefs are called *axioms*. The entire edifice of mathematical science is based upon axioms. More prevalently in the less rigid sciences, axioms actively expressing belief are known as *canons*, and from there, it's just a hop, skip, and a jump to fully feathered doctrine. However, let's not get beyond ourselves. At a fundamental level, axioms are unavoidable; it is only when entire theoretical structures (that is, *models*) are presented as axiomatic that the problem becomes insufferable.

In 1962, historian of science Thomas Kuhn published his landmark book, *The Structure of Scientific Revolutions*. In it, he coined a term that has become so widely used that it is almost a cliché: *paradigm shift*. In the context of this book, it refers to a revolutionary change in the assumptions employed in the practice of hard sciences, an overturning of the so-called standard models. The reason that standard models become as entrenched and zealously defended as they have been is sociological, and has almost nothing to do with physics or chemistry. Scientists, for all their bravado about objectivity, are after all as human as you or I, and demonstrate just the same passion for the canonisation of their opinions as politicians and religionists do. Sir Fred Hoyle put his own brand of witty cynicism on the matter: *"To hear scientists talk today, you would think the first moment in human history in which nonsensical views are not widely held is now."*

It is for this reason that, historically, paradigm shifts have been dreadfully slow in coming about. It's not that the science indicating change was weak; it's simply that the rulers of society, as in Church and Crown, have such an exaggerated aversion to being shown wrong. Politicians and clergy, it seems to me, would in many cases rather die than admit they were fundamentally incorrect in their assumptions; so when they reach out to take ownership of a scientific theory, heaven help us all.

For more than a thousand years, the paradigm known as geocentrism ruled the roost. From appearances alone, it seemed obvious that the Earth lay stationary at the centre of the universe, with all other celestial bodies revolving about it. This tied in rather nicely with the biblical view, so the science was therefore endorsed by the Church, and defended so harshly that critics were actually burned alive for daring to suggest otherwise. In the early 1500s, a canon of the Church, Nicolaus Copernicus, reconsidered the motions of objects on the sky, and came to the realisation that all was not as it seemed. The anomalies inherent in the standard cosmological model of the time could be more rationally explained if the Earth were not in fact standing still in the middle of it all, but indeed subservient to the Sun.

> The scorn which I had reason to fear on account of the novelty and unconventionality of my opinion almost induced me to abandon completely the work which I had undertaken. . . . Astronomy is written for astronomers. To them my work too will seem, unless I am mistaken, to make some contribution.
>
> Nicolaus Copernicus, Dedication to His Holiness Pope Paul III, preface to De revolutionibus orbium coelestium (On the Revolutions of the Heavenly Spheres), 1543

It was a terrifying thought, especially for poor Copernicus, a man of the cloth who was expected to toe the party line. He wrote his vision into his watershed book *On the Revolutions of Heavenly Spheres* and hid the manuscript in a box under his bed for more than thirty years. It was only as he lay dying on that very bed that he finally brought out his dark secret and requested that a sympathetic colleague have it published. He didn't have the model completely right — he retained some of Ptolemy's epicycles — but the fundamental principle was there: The Earth was not necessarily the biggest or most important thing in the cosmos. It obeyed an imperative from the Sun, which had power over it, and thus the roles were reversed. It was as if Copernicus had loosened the keystone in geocentrism's arch, and the walls of Jericho were about to come tumbling down. But as we by now well know, belief is not surrendered that easily.

A hundred years would pass, and many more martyrs would perish at the hands of those who wielded power, before sheer logic overwhelmed the dogma. Galileo was lucky to escape with his life, and it was only his popularity in Italian society that saved him from harsher punishment than house arrest and censorship.

> The proposition that the sun is the centre of the world and does not move from place to place is absurd and false philosophically and formally heretical, because it is expressively contrary to Holy Scripture. The proposition that the earth is not the centre of the world and immovable, but that it moves, and also with a diurnal motion, is equally absurd, philosophically false, and, theologically considered, at least erroneous in faith.
>
> *Sentence of the Tribunal of the Supreme*
> *Inquisition against Galileo Galilei, 22 June 1633*

Cosmology soon fell into an ideological vacuum. Heliocentrism brought with it the disconcerting corollary that we really didn't know very much after all. It seemed as far as science was concerned that the vastness of the unfolding universe defied a convenient, comfortable explanation. Religion had no such problem. The dominant theological explanation, involving supernatural forces and a creation *ex nihilo* at some point in the past was still tremendously popular, but beneath the cardinals' overt confidence lay a pressing need to replace geocentrism with a model that would fit the religious view. A Roman Catholic priest (and qualified astronomer) named Georges Lemâitre devised it. We now know it well by its colloquial name — Big Bang theory. The rest, as they say, is history.

Perhaps the first aspect of faith-driven behaviour to emerge from our investigation would be somewhat comical were it not for an inevitable tragedy lying deeper in the script. Let's face it, beliefs cause people to do crazy stuff — *but only according to other people holding other beliefs.* That might sound like stating the obvious, but it's crucial to getting a clear grasp of the nature of the animal we are studying. We hold our own beliefs in high esteem, and regard opposing, contradictory opinions as false, or at least "less true" or inferior to our own. It's as if we award ourselves some kind of divine privilege. Of all the beliefs in the entire world, ours is the right one. Of all the spiritual connections in the universe, mine is the one that brings the right answer. Of all the imagined models in the entire history of science, the one I like is the most accurate. After having made that damning declaration, we then set out to find the evidence. And find it we will.

Beliefs play a vital role in the validation of self. The vision we have of ourselves is so glued to our beliefs that sharing these convictions takes on a missionary zeal. I share — maybe even impose — my beliefs on you, in the poignant hope that you will recognise that I am speaking the truth. It is important to me that you do — not only that you embrace my articles of faith as profound wisdom, but also that you remember always that you learnt it from me.

If a reader of this book says to me, "Wow. That is so true," I am validated and my self-esteem brightens appreciably. I expressed a set of opinions, you cried hallelujah, and in an instant I am whole again. The opposite is equally true. If my profound truth is exposed for what it really is, merely a tenuous opinion subject potentially to falsification, I am quickly despondent. And defensive.

A belief is essentially a conclusion; a believer accepts changes only to expand and reinforce his preferred paradigm. He does not sincerely entertain criticism, but instead most often becomes immediately defensive. Whenever a person presents a model with the assertion that all tenets of the model are indisputably correct, we can safely assume that he is expressing belief. It is not science. Settled science is a myth. The protagonist invests his ego in the model, and is thereby bound to defend it. Thus we have ownership leading to instinctive defence.

I hope I have made this clear — it is our *ownership* of the idea that makes it good, not whether or not it is inherently true or survives stringent empirical testing. I concede that this may be a little difficult to wrap our intuition around, but please mull over it. The instinctive roots of believing are exposed here, revealing a distinct parallel with territorial and tribal imperatives: My property, my country, my tribe are better than yours, and I'm prepared to fight for them. The half acre on this side of my garden fence is in no objective way superior to the half acre on my neighbour's side, but I prefer mine because it's mine. I prefer my belief and opinion to yours for the same reason. It's *mine*. This separates belief from the scientific ideal, and also brings under scrutiny a defining property of belief: It is purely and simply an expression of our sanctified self-image, in a word, egotism.

The power of ownership — whether of fixed property or intellectual assets — shows up in no uncertain terms when it is under threat. As proprietors, we treat belief no differently from territory or progeny, and instinctively defend it just as vigorously. We ought by now to sense a clue in differentiating between belief and objective science: When an idea, theory, or model is promoted and justified with zeal, it is a sure sign that it has regressed to belief. Negotiating about belief with an evangelical believer becomes so difficult that it verges on the impossible. Belief insulates its owner from rational analysis, and puts a charge of adrenalin into his veins when his turn comes to occupy the pulpit. Proselytising belief is a form of intellectual imperialism.

A very good illustration of the passion of ownership came in recent years in the form of theoretical physicist Luboš Motl. Originally from the Czech Republic, Motl received his PhD in mathematics from Rutgers University in the United States. He made it as far as a staff position at Harvard University before he fell from grace. He was subsequently "let go" from Harvard under a cloud that follows him still. Motl returned to the Czech Republic in 2007, and (much to my relief) has not published anything about string theory since then.

It was during his years at Harvard that Motl started his notorious blog, "*Luboš Motl's Reference Frame*", and it was really his crass manner that got him into trouble. The root of his discourtesy is his passionate belief in string theory, along with its offshoots and subsets including supersymmetry, superstring theory, the clutch of ideas known as M-theory, and the mathematical reasoning that allows

apparently sane people to assert that the universe is constructed in eleven or more spatial dimensions. He describes
himself as a Christian atheist — go figure! In 2004, I visited
Harvard to chat about evolution with the inspirational biologist Professor Ernst Mayr. Quite by accident, I came face
to face with the man made famous by his abrasive character and boorish communication skills. By the skin of my
teeth, I managed to avoid punching Motl in the face, so
disagreeable is he, but that's a story for another fireside and
a fresh pot of tea.

What lay behind this arch-geek's poor bedside manner?
Let me tell you what I think it is. Of the current generation
of mathematical theorists, one I admire most is Dr Peter
Woit. I have had the pleasure of corresponding with him
on matters of physics, although by my definition he is not
in any sense a physicist. Dr Woit was one of the prime mov-
ers of string theory before he came to his senses, and I pick
up the story in chapter 12 of *The Virtue of Heresy*:

Are we to believe that mathematics can tell us what
the essential underlying principles of the universe are,
and furthermore, can do it in their entirety? We firmly
refute that notion. Take it from somebody who should
know. Professor of mathematics Peter Woit of Colum-
bia University spent more than 20 years completely
immersed in the search for the Theory of Everything.
After graduating from Harvard in 1979, Woit went
on to take a doctorate in theoretical physics from
Princeton. An Ivy League career in teaching physics
followed, and true to the way that our graduate school
curricula are organised, Dr Woit was classically con-

ditioned to trade common sense for the more elitist practice of metamathematics. In 2006, he could take it no more. It was as if he awoke, rubbed the sleep from his eyes, and for the first time saw how the sirens of mathematical sorcery had lured him onto the rocks. He wrote a kiss-and-tell book called *Not Even Wrong*, in which he exposes the movement as a thinly veneered religious cult, with all the negative connotations that such a description embraces.

Overly dramatic? No way! Read the book[2]. From the point of view of a well-qualified and highly positioned insider, Peter Woit shows with an engaging lack of malice that superstring theory is not a theory at all. Since its inception in the early 80s, it has made no testable predictions at all, not even wrong ones. Another Harvard graduate, renowned theorist Dr Lee Smolin concurs with us. He too published a book in 2006, called *The Trouble with Physics*,[3] in which he cogently argues that out-of-touch mathematicians have led physics, the basis of all physical science, astray. A former leading string theorist, Lee Smolin is as well positioned as anyone to tell it like it is. Professor Woit has been there, Dr Smolin has been there, and so have I, and I don't think we *could* exaggerate the fierce psychological entrapment, the irresistible illusion of

---

2 Peter Woit, *Not Even Wrong: The Failure of String Theory and the Search for Unity in Physical Law* (New York: Basic Books, 2006).

3 Lee Smolin, *The Trouble with Physics: The Rise of String Theory, The Fall of a Science, and What Comes Next* (New York: Houghton Mifflin, 2006).

power that comes from losing oneself in the splendid isolation of mathematical fluency. It is a psychological dependency that feeds off the feeling of superiority and messianic untouchability that surrounds the thrones of those who, by virtue of no more than their arcane mathematical argot delude themselves and us that they understand something we don't.[4]

The fringe online disinformation site RationalWiki, which seems to specialise in character assassination, must have been delighted when Luboš Motl emerged from obscurity. His controversial character is manna from heaven for RationalWiki. This is an excerpt from their Motl page:

> The problem is his refusal to recognize that his sphere of competence is finite. And God help you if you've ever implied *anywhere* that string theory is anything less than the revealed secret of the universe, particularly if you're Lee Smolin, Peter Woit or *'similar breathtakingly dishonest far-left anti-scientific subhuman activist garbage'.*

It should be clear that Woit and Smolin are directly opposed to the position held by Motl, just as he is to theirs. The point relevant to our study in this book is that they did not try with calm reason to settle their differences. At least, Motl did not. In this debate, both Peter Woit and Lee

---

4 Hilton Ratcliffe, *The Virtue of Heresy: Confessions of a Dissident Astronomer* (Create Space, 2008).

Smolin, as I know them, have not so much as raised their voices. Motl, by contrast, spent the whole time shouting. In my opinion, his unbridled zeal stems directly from his *belief* that he has the privilege of truth. If he was simply convinced by the facts, he would have no need to shout. It his ownership of the theory that gives him the right, the divine duty almost, to defend the M-theory model at all costs, no matter whom he hurts in the process. That's not science; it's self-righteous conviction.

If we pay attention to the way we promulgate belief, we begin to understand the role it plays in scientific models, and ultimately, why science and religion belong in separate classrooms. I want to emphasise that our study seeks to address belief in a secular way, and delineate its role in secular matters particularly. For a number of reasons, I wish by all means to avoid reducing this investigation to an argument about religion. At the same time, it is simply not scholarly to leave religion out of contention as a source of case studies.

Belief *belongs* in religion; there, it enjoys a welcoming, compatible environment in which to flourish. It is where we can find prime examples to illustrate the driving principles. Religionists are charmingly open about their propensity for belief, and seem proud of it. Scientists are quite the opposite. They most often recoil in horror and indignation at the suggestion that they too are believers. It is consequently far easier to find the examples we're looking for in theism, where they are openly displayed, than it is in scientism, where they are hidden away.

Given that, it is my intention to be broadly catholic in my choice of examples and analogues. I shall be using cases that fairly plumb both religious faith and secular philosophies. In those instances where I do use examples from religion, they will be drawn from the entire array of religions without fear or favour.

At a fundamental level, in their reflection of first principles, beliefs found in atheism, Islam, cosmology, or Christianity are in no essential aspect different from one another. They differ only in the way they express detail; at their roots, they are astonishingly similar. And that, my friends, is what makes my mission so difficult to achieve. Believers in any of the four faiths cited above, if they are reasonable, rational people, will readily accept this basic commonality to be true. However, they invariably preface their reasonableness with the caveat that the particular group they belong to personally is the single exception.

Atheists are quick to imply that they have no belief, but they're wrong. They believe that there is no God, although their assertion can never be proven true. Muslims spawn a high proportion of radical extremists within their ranks, based upon the premise that theirs is the one true faith, but in the opinion of this writer, they are just as misguided as the atheists. Somehow, sooner rather than later, we must come to the realisation that our own belief is not the exception to the rule, thereby stripping the implied sense of divinity from what is in reality no more than our fragile point of view, fiercely held.

Following on this, it becomes clear that religion is simply a special case of the belief syndrome. Religion is a belief system in which the "Dark Energy" takes the form of a deity (or set of deities) that possesses an array of attributes drawn most often from accounts of ancient legend. The mystery of the origin and sustenance of the cosmos is seldom faced with the admission of "I don't know"; we meet it instead with a solution derived from belief.

Religion takes the imposition of intuitive belief significantly further than we would expect from secular explanations. Faith arrays the postulated primal energy with richly detailed, human-like qualities. In the English versions of Christianity and Judaism, for example, it is called God, and it has a remarkably familiar face. God, we are told by those in the know, presents itself in the form of a male human being, with a personality very much like our own. Thus we have He who created the universe *ex nihilo*, and governs it for our exclusive benefit with love, anger, mercy, egotism, violence, cruelty, sexual perversion, and cynicism. Sound familiar? In a further subset of this overarching theology, He even begets a child (a son, of course), whom He condemns to a macabre, paranormal death to make His point.

None of these attributes comes from rational deduction based on testable observation, nor do they follow logically from our confrontation of the cosmological mystery. In other words, we did not get this knowledge from empirical science, nor can we subject it to scientific verification or deduce it from what we see. Although secular and religious beliefs operate on the same principles, with more or less the same outcomes, religion distinguishes itself by being far more comfortable and open about allowing imagination to fill in the blanks.

Belief is a powerful agency. It shapes our thinking and guides our behaviour to such an extent that we often become blind to the chicanery of snake oil charlatans.

We sometimes allow our adulation to turn us into factories blithely manufacturing imaginary evidence to support premises founded upon nothing more than illusion. My examination of the accounts of witnesses seems to indicate that their convictions often emerge from an improper association of ideas rather than the uttering of a blatant lie. Above all, believers believe themselves, and that causes them to artificially associate unrelated phenomena. Thus, as examples, we find people correlating their prayers with a particular outcome, to the exclusion of other more feasible explanations. Then there are the "sighters". There is an endless supply of eager witnesses who have apparently convinced themselves that the shadowy figure with a well-oiled quiff and large, bling shades is beyond doubt Elvis Presley, resurrected.

For someone swaddled in the comfort of such faith, the illusion remains completely indiscernible. We have literally fallen under a spell. What stymied me in my research was not so much the white lies of sycophants as their persistence — sometimes unto death — in defence of falsehoods that they must surely have been aware of at some deeper level of the psyche. Making up a story that you have seen Elvis alive in downtown Spokane is one thing; completely abandoning your faculty to self-audit your own integrity is quite another.

We should isolate and emphasise this point: *Devotees who are intoxicated by belief will invariably fabricate evidence in support of their beliefs.* More alarming still, they appear to have no qualms about subjectively bending the truth. What they wish to be true blurs what is actually true, so the well-meaning witness appears to have no moral compunction at all. By their ethics, saying that I saw the Abominable Snowman is not morally wrong if I truly believe in it, and more importantly, if I passionately wish others to believe in it too. In other words, it is the scepticism of non-believers that is the bad thing here, not the little fib or three that I invoke in our quest to put humankind on the right track.

This type of moral self-justification is pervasive and resilient. It progresses without a second thought from unreservedly promoting the doctrine of the chosen authority in the field, to claiming to have personally witnessed an unexplained, other-worldly phenomenon in support of that doctrine, to actually forging photographs that purport to show Bigfoot in Nepal, or UFOs in New Mexico, or faith healers restoring sight to the blind, or carbon dioxide warming the Earth; in the rare atmosphere of angels, the end unashamedly justifies the means. The barefaced lies are usually perpetrated by those high up in the hierarchy, most often by the leaders of cults themselves, with their senior disciples being complicit more by providing support for their master's deception than by lying themselves. Nevertheless, we cannot ignore the fact that zealous believers all too frequently promulgate deliberate untruths as part of their evangelical duty. In the hands of self-aggrandised moral warriors, it is a terrible thing indeed. Beneath their flowing white robes, they are no more than sanctified confidence tricksters. Yet we flock in our millions to believe in them and bear witness to their miracles. Why?

In my early years as a student, I came across the works of a nineteenth- century German theologian named Max

Müller, and he became iconic in my understanding of belief. He introduced me to a concept he named the *dialogic process*, and I had one of those moments when a light comes on in your head and the shadows retreat. I held Müller's idea firmly in my mind's grip, and it was awe-inspiring.

It seemed to me that between his mental fingertips, Dr Müller held a seed, pregnant with meaning. Not only was he able to classify in a clear way a whole chunk of human behaviour involving adulation, he was also, I came to believe, able to explain the underlying justification for all of religion. He articulated the principle that leads us to proclaim — with great conviction — that wondrous thing we have no solid, rational reason to believe is true.

Even more pertinently, the dialogic process reveals why disciples, seemingly without contradicting their personal ethics, exaggerate or even outright lie about the focus of their sycophantic belief. He explained with one almost nonchalant sweep of his hand all phenomena accompanying the utterances of disciples: Walking on water, the sightings of Elvis, faith healing, interaction with UFOs, the Jonestown suicides, witnessing Christ's resurrection, and finding 300-year-old ascetics in the Himalayas who live on air.

It also gave me a glimmer of understanding, for the first time, why the "blinding light" experiences of people with strongly developed belief instincts — call them epiphanies, revelations, voice of God, whatever suits you — could return such differing, even contradictory understandings of life and the universe. It was momentous, a watershed. I didn't run naked from my bath yelling *"Eureka!"* but I wasn't far off.

Such as it is, it [the Dialogic Process] will give us an insight into the way in which a new religion, or rather a new sect, springs up and grows. It will place before our eyes the transformation which mere repetition, conversation, or what is called oral tradition will and must produce in the description of the facts as they really happened. We can watch here what is really a kind of Dialectic Process which is at work in all history, both ancient and modern. This Dialectic Process as applied to the facts of history comprehends all the changes which are inevitably produced by the mere communication and interchange of ideas, by the give and take of dialogue, by the turning of thoughts from one side to the other.

Whatever the origin of a religion may be supposed to have been, its growth from the very first depends clearly on the recipient soil, that is, on human nature, and to study that human nature as it reacts on religion is one of the most useful lessons of Comparative Theology. [...] discloses here and there the clear traces of what I call the Dialogic Process, and the irrepressible miraculising tendencies of devoted disciples. And I am really glad that it does so, if only it helps to teach us that no historian can ever pretend to do more than to show us what a man or a fact seemed to be to him or to the authorities whom he has to follow, and not what he or it actually was.

Max Müller, The Dialogic Process, from
Ramakrishna, His Life and Works.

What Max Müller succeeded in doing where so many had failed was to lend formal legitimacy and scholarly recognition to a sociological condition that most of us prefer to avoid mentioning. The dialogic process refers to a character trait that appears to affect almost everyone possessed by their beliefs: The irresistible urge to glorify the deeds of their master, and consequently to report events surrounding their adopted doctrine in such glowing terms that their account exceeds common sense (and any empirical testing which might occasionally have been done) by a wide margin. It is certainly a ubiquitous phenomenon and characterises religions and cults of all persuasions, and at all epochs of history.

Belief, as we have defined it, is a principle, opinion, or conviction adopted without proof, or a proof accepted prior to validation. An article of belief forms a personal axiom. Reference to supporting (secular) evidence is entirely optional. There are people of enormously strong faith who raise no argument whatsoever to justify their faith. Belief is intellectually reinforced not so much by rational thought as by classical conditioning, and consequently indoctrination plays a vitally important role in all belief organisations. We all have belief at a personal level, but as soon as it becomes socially organised, imprinting of the doctrine follows. It's easy (and misleading) to dismiss this kind of mental conditioning as belonging only to isolated religious extremism. It is pervasive. Even the most mild-mannered, rustic religious sects habitually practice indoctrination in the course of their ceremonial devotions. Ideology seeks to dominate, and there is hardly a degree of variation between the methods employed by religious sects, theoretical physicists, and ruling political parties.

Let's examine the phenomenon more closely and try to determine its global appeal. Are beliefs useful in the social milieu? How do they reward us? If the need to believe is, as I suggest, a cellular, instinctive imperative, then it would typically carry its own reward mechanism. The drive to procreate is sweetened by the sensual pleasure of sexual activity surrounding intercourse. In the build-up to mating with the partner of our desires, we have been known to lie through our teeth without batting an eyelid. Afterwards, when our lust has abated and the thrill of the chase has gone to sleep, our sense of propriety returns, and we may even openly regret the deception we employed to satisfy the sexual instinct. At the time, however, we don't give it a second thought. It's as if instinct (or belief) grants us a temporary, higher morality that quite overrules the ethics we observe when we are sober.

This type of reward system is self-serving. It satisfies itself. It creates the very need that it purports to sate. I have for many years been involved in helping drug addicts back to health, and my experience suggests that addiction is an aberration of belief. A cigarette smoker holds beliefs about his habit that quite clearly fail independent, objective validation. For example, he would typically argue in defence of his behaviour that smoking calms his nerves. Technically, in a very narrow view, he's right; smoking a cigarette does alleviate a sense of discomfort he feels at the time. In a wider, more balanced view, however, it is obvious that the nervousness he wants so badly to appease is simply a withdrawal symptom. Nicotine addiction creates the need it seeks to satisfy, in a closed loop. This is true of the belief syndrome generally.

Arguably, the keystone that locks the secret of belief is the matter of motivation: *Why* do we adopt a particular belief and not another? What is it about the presentation of a model that we find so convincing that we willingly seam-weld it into our personal dogma?

THERE ARE MANY influences. I shall list some of them here:

- *Empathy with the author.* She would be inspirational and charismatic, probably having overcome daunting personal challenges like health crises and persecution. Their personal circumstances evoke public sympathy, and project a sense of martyrdom. Examples: Jill Bolte Taylor, Julian Assange, Immanuel Velikovsky.
- *Moral subterfuge.* The issue would present itself as holding some or other moral or ethical high ground. Examples: climate change activism, conspiracy cults, Marxism.
- A *key-in to existing prejudice, especially as manifested in educational bias.* Examples: standard model dogma, opposition to, or support of, Darwinian evolution.
- *Adulation.* Sycophantic fanaticism will quickly canonise the presenter of a popularly believed model. Examples: John

Lennon, Albert Einstein, William Lane Craig.

- *Authority*. Belief stems always from perceived authority, be it NASA, God, or self (religion). Authority is accepted from the presenter of the model itself, or the presenter as an agent of remote higher authority, for example, ancient prophets, CIA, aliens. Subservience to perceived authority is at the top of an idea stack, the lower tiers contributing a priori to the initial choice of authority figure. Examples: Barack Obama, Stephen Hawking, Sam Harris, Prophet Muhammed.
- *"Evidence."* This is a subset of authority. Belief is an evidence factory, and contrived, artificial evidence plays a significant role in propaganda and indoctrination. It ranges from the unverifiable interpretation of experimental data (with arguably the worst offenders being neuroscience and particle physics) to outright fabrication. Examples: discovery of the Higgs boson (God particle), explicit pictures of thoughts in cerebral scans.
- *Charisma*. Cult heroes have overt charisma. It's an irrational X factor that gives them their hypnotic persuasiveness. Examples: Rasputin, Albert Einstein, William Lane Craig, Carl Sagan, Adolph Hitler.

- *Untruth*. In belief systems, the end justifies the means. Lies are morally justified by the perceived sanctity of the greater message. Authority figures will lie without qualms, whether by exaggeration, omission, or even by explicit fabrication, to reinforce their position. In many cases the lie is carried by no more than clever editing. Followers of belief systems, who play a vital role in promulgating those untruths, have great difficulty accepting what I'm saying, but it remains arguably the most prevalent characteristic of belief-motivated individuals. Examples: Jim Jones's People's Temple cult, politicians, conspiracy theorists, cosmologists.
- *Mystery*. Focus on specific global mysteries, real or perceived, is a powerful motivator of belief. Examples: conspiracy theories, UFOlogy, Egyptology, Big Bang theory, religion.
- *Desire to transcend the mundane and feel in some way special*. Belief is a powerful medication for individuals who feel trapped by an ordinary existence and the daily grind of the rat race. Examples: drugs, cults, gangs.
- *Exclusive truth*. Belief systems are usually based upon a point of view that claims privileged insight to mystery. Examples: relativity, M-theory, religion, sects, secret societies, cosmology, metamathematics.

- *Encryption*. The mystery is enhanced by some level of arcane code. Examples: general relativity, Mormonism, Freemasons, Egyptology.
- *Muzak and piggyback*. If the model makes all the right sounds, lulling us into a self-reinforcing comfort zone, it succeeds. A popular ploy is to use scientific jargon and officious statistics to give the idea a ring of objective authenticity. Examples: anthropogenic global warming, Michael Moore documentaries, political campaign tickets, astrology, Scientology.
- *Propaganda and dogma*. The sociopolitical organisation of belief is characterised by the overt use of propaganda, conditioning, and proselytising, and by the dogmatic stance of proponents. These are two of the more clearly defined properties of belief in action. Examples: apologists, Roman Catholic Church, Big Bang theory.
- *The pack instinct*: mobs and gangsterism[5]. Gangsters will do things at immense personal risk without any supporting rationale other than blind allegiance to the gang. The model is seen to be the only viable world view under the circumstances.

---

5 *Gangsterism* refers to the sociological phenomenon exemplified by modern street gangs, viz., an extreme pack reaction to social rejection and unrequited social or economic circumstances. It is a manifestation of the us-versus-them pack-binding ethic.

     Examples, Hell's Angels, white supremacists, al-Qaeda.

- *Bandwagon.* Many good ideas and research projects are given enhanced viability by attachment to a popular, dominant model. Example: independent research on coral reefs gets linked to climate change, Roman Catholic Church endorses Big Bang theory.
- *The eternal devil's advocate.* Many beliefs are driven by the satisfaction some find in being an iconoclast, a rebellious author of the consequently derived "anti-belief". Examples: conspiracy theories, political opposition, climate change deniers, militant atheists.

It is clear that belief is an instinctual compulsion, a primordial need for comfort, security against the unknown. Whatever form it may take, we all have it, without exception as far as I can tell. We are born with two dominant fears — falling and separation. Both are survival instincts related to powers greater than ourselves; the first acknowledges gravitation, and the second, a symbiotic connection to the divine mother. Neither is dressed up in robes or masked in swirling incense. We add those rituals and reinforcing superstitions later, when the need to be right dominates our more mature outlook. In the heat of false security, we tend to forget that we are all just children of the universe, scratching like fowls in the dirt of knowledge. Information is a jumble of words hiding shreds of truth; there are nuggets in the sludge, sure, but overall, it's sludge.

Let's get this clear in our minds: Belief *precedes* intellectual analysis and directs the course of our thinking from there on in. We are somehow predisposed to certain opinions and biases, and these are so powerful that they anonymously take over the direction of our lives. Please bear in mind that we are talking only about *tendencies*, not explicit opinions. None of us is born Republican or communist or Muslim; our justification for being any of those things comes after the fact. We are viscerally supporters of Big Bang theory (or detractors of the theory, as the case may be) long before we first ever articulate, or indeed even hear of the supporting evidence. The Prophet Muhammed was already polygamous by the time scriptural edict sanctifying polygamy first appeared in Islam.

Belief is not obtained rationally, nor does it depend upon the believer being clever or being stupid. It emerges from a deep intuitive connection to something extra-conscious. Some beliefs are obviously more aligned with objective truth than others, but that is irrelevant to the believer, who holds his belief irrespective of whether it correlates with someone else's conception of truth. *In effect, belief defines one's idea of what is really true.* Now that's a scary thought, isn't it?

We don't need to know the origin or cause of a phenomenon in order to understand and quantify its effect on our lives and our environment; gravitation is a good example of well-understood effects of an unknown cause. If we can fully embrace a spirit of pragmatism, it would be clear that our stubbornly determined quest for an origin of everything we study is a distraction that should more sensibly be left for the very end of our investigation, where philosophical implications can be mused upon at leisure, over a cup of tea.

What *causes* gravitation and what it *is*, are philosophical questions. What it does to us and how it affects objects in our observable environment, on the other hand, are not. They are matters of pure physics. We can observe and measure it and it's the same for all of us, no matter what we believe. If you and your neighbour's dog measure the effect of gravity as I jump off my roof, you'll both get the same answer, every time. Thus, it is a defining property of the common reality that we share in and that treats us all without prejudice.

The most important message I wish to convey in the pages before you is that we *all* have belief. I shouldn't think it possible for a mind to function without incorporating a point of view that was obtained by some means other than rational deduction from first principles. The human psyche receives consistent input that may be described as visceral, gut feel, intuitive, or plain common sense. By accepting this universality of belief as an axiom, we can proceed further down the sticky path of unravelling the generally constraining effects of belief, before finally applying these tenets to our own dogma. The essential caveat to our study is twofold: We should not put our own personal beliefs under the microscope (I shall expand on this as we go along); and we should not, in respect of any of the beliefs we are about to dissect, concern ourselves with whether the notion being put forward by the believer is right or wrong in any absolute sense. We shall concentrate at this stage on training ourselves to recognise belief and distinguish it clearly from objective data and measurements.

Here's an interesting thought — all else being equal, who would we prefer as president of the United States, an atheist or a Mormon? It's a question I can't answer easily. That choice is not what Americans had to make in 2012 of course; Obama is not an atheist, but it does illuminate the problem. Democracy works properly if we choose leaders for their qualities of leadership and their integrity. On the other hand, democracy goes awry if we choose leaders simply because they are aligned with our personal belief system, or worse, if we reject one of two candidates only because he opposes some of our superstitions. In this hypothetical scenario, my gut tells me immediately to favour the atheist, because in my personal beliefs I am more aligned with atheism than I am with Mormonism, but after pondering the matter, I don't think that's the wisest approach.

For all their daft ideas, Mormons do in principle at least espouse some qualities that I would like to see in a leader. I have been to Salt Lake City, and I was mightily impressed with what they have achieved in the name of their faith. The same cannot be said for atheism, which has no ideology or doctrine, and certainly no monumental cathedral or heavenly choir. In the 2012 presidential race, neither candidate was obviously more or less moral than the other as far as I could see from an ocean away, so the choice should have been made independently of emotive factors like brand of faith, race, or looks. It should have, but it wasn't. That's just a pipe dream.

Recently, we had the rise of the 2012 doomsday movement, an extraordinarily potent example of the need for belief. It brings to mind the picture of dying man in a baking desert who falls unexpectedly into an oasis pool, and slakes his ravenous thirst as if there's no tomorrow. No matter how muddy the water, it seems perfectly clear to believers. Our thirst renders it clear. Americans are crazy about surveys, and the results of surveys on the 2012 doomsday legend are fascinating. I have no doubt that other nations show similar tendencies, probably in proportion to their information quotient, but the American model is fine for our purposes. Joe and Joan Citizen in the United States tell us that:

- A bomb shelter is a wiser investment than a retirement policy (41%).
- The ancient Mayans predicted an apocalypse, and it will come true (27%).
- Nearly half of Americans are making contingency plans: stocking up on canned goods (45%), laying up bottled water (55%), keeping a hoard of cash (24%), and breeding post-apocalyptic livestock (6%).

By the time you read this, you will have seen that it was just a load of twaddle, but the glaringly important point to be taken from all this is that half of Americans fell for it. A highly educated nation, in command of cutting-edge technology, and with greater access to information than any other fell into a state of lifestyle-altering belief. It was not founded on any reasonable, rational fact of any shape, size, or form. Yet we believed. Why?

A friend who became a disciple and evangelist for the world view of Jill Bolte Taylor hit the nail on the head when I asked him *why* he believed what she was telling us:

"Because it made sense."[6] With those few words, my understanding of belief leapt the quantum leap. That's it. Our
reception of a proposed model's data passes first through
a visceral filter, and we let our common sense set the tone
before (or even whether or not) we investigate the empirical validity of what is being proposed. That gut feel is
powerful enough to fully circumvent stringent objective
testing of a theory before it is embraced as belief. Prior to
the Copernican revolution, common sense provided ready
support for the notion that the Earth was the central pivot
of a rotating universe, and it took protracted effort, frac-
tured by bloody persecution and institutional resistance, to
roll it over.

The same is true of parents with severely handicapped,
critically ill children. Their desperate search to find anything at all that would relieve their child's suffering is
truly heart-rending. Failures of conventional medicine are
cursed with as much venom as the alleged successes of
snake oil receive their praise. They clutch anxiously at a
quack's dangled straws, quite oblivious to the fraud they are
being sold. Emotion drives their free will into fully fledged
belief to such a degree that they will swear they have seen
miracles. The consequence is that as a rule, emotion will
trump pragmatism, every time a coconut.

I should hope that we can all in due course recognise
that testing science is altogether more demanding and

---

6 Jill Bolte Taylor is a popular neuroscientist who has used her personal
experience with a debilitating stroke (and concomitant near-death experience) to promote a theory that posits consciously deliberate left-brain/
right-brain self-manipulation to secure mental health.

rigorous than that. Don't get me wrong — it is entirely impracticable (and, no doubt, unnecessary) to dissect every data input with an electron microscope. The critical breaking point is not so much developing an opinion as a result of gut feel; that's perfectly acceptable and practically harmless. The problem really makes itself felt when a particular, hastily adopted opinion becomes the baseline for a hypo-stack. If a tenet of theory that has been derived from sixth sense only is used to hold up the framework of a burgeoning model, the stress is massive. That's exactly what happened with geocentrism: Common sense told the ancients that the Sun went about the Earth, and from that innocent assumption came forth a whole paradigm, replete with epicycles and elegant sophistry.

It became clear to me in an instant that my friend slipped so easily into the Taylor fan club simply because of a pre-existing inclination to believe that sort of thing. It was an answer he *wanted* to be true, and that was enough. Sincerely, with great conviction and kind, selfless motivation, he tried to convert me (for my own good) to a model that remained factually unproven.

It also occurred to me over tea with my friend that if we are reasonably well acquainted with someone's outlook on life (his *presets*), we can with fair accuracy predict which ideas he might readily buy into. We do this all the time in political sociology — by dividing people up into opposing camps named conservative and liberal, we can stereotype them in terms of their beliefs. It is often surprisingly accurate.

The grip of belief on one's world view became clearer when dialogue revealed more of his point of view. It's story time. Every so often, an individual pops up somewhere in the world who has a fantastic affinity with nature. We think of George Adamson and the *Born Free* lions, Steve Irwin talking to his Australian reptiles, Dian Fossey living with the mountain gorillas of Rwanda, and Eugène Marais experiencing the soul of termites. More recently, we had here in KwaZulu-Natal, South Africa, an amazing naturalist named Lawrence Anthony. There is no doubt that he was a gifted man of the bush, and he deservedly became an icon in local wildlife circles. His empathy with elephants was so well-developed that it wasn't long before he acquired the honorary nickname *Elephant Whisperer*, ultimately the title of his popular biographical novel published in 2011. Pretty soon, Lawrence Anthony was walking on water.

Our tendency as believing creatures is to selectively review the pristine data so that it harmonises with our presets. When Lawrence Antony died, so the legend goes, elephants at some distance from his homestead were immediately aware of it. They gathered in a solemn vigil at his house. It's a beautiful story, but how much of it is strictly true? We see a photograph of elephants proceeding down a footpath. Everything else is garnishing. The telepathic correlation with Lawrence Anthony's sudden and unexpected death is the product of what we like to believe about the Elephant Whisperer and about the sentimentally romantic elephants of our mind's eye. The evidence factory slips into high gear, and the story becomes more astonishing by the minute. We *make* it work because that's what pleases us. On the barest smidgen of evidence, we'll blithely construct a hypothesis, then a theory, then a model, and then in a final, inevitable act of nonsense, we see so much reality in the model that it transforms from a collection of ideas to become the frame around our world view.

The idea-construct becomes in itself a proxy for objective truth. The corollary (as important to truth as the theorem itself) is that our defence of the mental picture we carry to the fore is strengthened and rendered into dogma because it is held as a hallowed thought; *it* is morally right, and *we* are morally right, and that circumvents the need — and, indeed, the *desire* — for sterile, disinfected analysis.

We have to own up to the fact that we create evidence to support preferred belief. What's more, if we are brutally honest with ourselves, we'll see that even if we are not the actual authors of the myth, we are complicit by our eager and premature acceptance of stories that twinge our heartstrings with such convincing charm that we thereafter proselytise and hypo-stack those mentalisms with gay abandon.

The crucial point is this: Opinions held within and because of a belief paradigm, however articulately they may be presented, and irrespective of mathematical elegance in their justification, are inherently unreliable. The degree to which we believe in Big Bang theory and the intrinsic quality of a thousand pages of formalism raised in support, does not mean that it actually happened as a real event in history. The passion with which we believe in the Bible does not make Noah's Ark factually true, or even likely for that matter. The fanaticism with which we hate Bush's America while at the same time sanctifying our own unique cleverness in getting the inside track, in no way validates the 9/11 conspiracy theories. Quite the contrary, in fact.

Belief acts as an agency to hold our rational thought tightly unto itself. Truth becomes, for as long as that particular faith rules our thinking, merely an internal artefact in a closed logical loop. It insulates itself from reality so cleverly that followers *want* to become martyrs in some sense or another.

Author Libba Bray, in her book *The Sweet Far Thing*, said "You must remember, my dear lady, the most important rule of any successful illusion: First, the people must want to believe in it."

There you have it.

> *What is wanted is not the will to believe, but the will to find out, which is the exact opposite.*
>
> BERTRAND RUSSELL

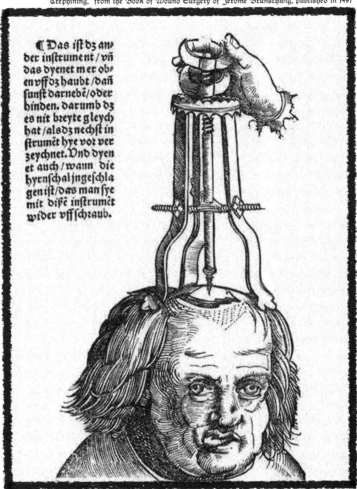

e are stimulated by the idea that we have the vision to see past the veil of stupidity that smothers global opinions other than our own, and consequently claim for ourselves the moral victory of truth.

5

SCEPTICISM AND PRAGMATISM

Do we know what we're talking about?

WHILST SOME OF MY philosophy has stemmed from healthy scepticism, I had to return to my roots to discover what I was really looking for: a school of thought founded in applied pragmatism. My father, a practical physicist and down-to-earth thinker, and my grandfather, an amateur astronomer and connoisseur of fine things, were powerful influences on me from birth. The way that they explained nature to me was a delight that I cannot properly describe, and it was particularly my father's clear grasp of Newtonian mechanics that stamped me irrevocably as a cause-and-effect sort of chap.

I have given my approach to natural philosophy the label *scientific pragmatism*, and this quote from Steven Pinker sums it up beautifully:

As a young teenager in proudly peaceable Canada during the romantic 1960s, I was a true believer in Bakunin's anarchism. I laughed off my parents' argument that if the government ever laid down its arms all hell would break loose. Our competing predictions were put to the test at 8:00 A.M. on October 17, 1969, when the Montreal police went on strike. This decisive empirical test left my politics in tatters (and offered a foretaste of life as a scientist).[1]

Pinker experienced a clear empirical test of his hypotheses, and had the good sense to understand how well he'd been debunked. No matter how strongly we hold our theoretical convictions, and quite irrespective of the devoutness of our faith, reality in the form of human nature has a way from time to time of irreverently clouting us alongside the earhole. Not for nothing is it called a reality check. Centuries of civilisation and cultured etiquette give way in an instant to the turgid viscosity of subconscious cellular imperatives, if circumstances require it. Free will cannot hold a candle to instinct, but it can do something very, very important: It allows us some freedom to choose the way we deal with facts. Free will permits us the faculty of scepticism.

Scepticism has shifted the hierarchy of tools the unbiased scientist must use. Not very long ago, it was no more than an entertaining but minor inflection on the methodology of science; now, it has in my view emerged as the

---

1 Steven Pinker, *The Blank Slate: The Modern Denial of Human Nature* (New York: Penguin Putnam, 2002).

only thing that can save our objective knowledge base from implosion. Without it we are lost, with no more control on the outcome than a roller-coaster ride. Response to scepticism by the orthodoxy is invariably reactionary; it's a damned nuisance, actually, for those for whom the standard curriculum is what puts bread onto the table. Scepticism slows everything down, and whilst I fully understand why that's bad news for academics trying to get their flock to graduate, for researchers unravelling the secrets of nature, it's absolutely essential. In my experience, there is nothing that's more damning of useable truth in scientific endeavour than unseemly haste. The unchecked speed with which the canon grows condemns us to the pursuit of doctrine by indoctrination.

I titled my first book *The Virtue of Heresy: Confessions of a Dissident Astronomer*. That ought to tell you something. The title implies that the heretic is virtuous and does a good thing by being disobedient. Science legend Dick Feynman called science "the culture of doubt" and I heartily concur. Science progresses not by agreement, but by being challenged. The frontiers of knowledge are pushed forward by those who dare to explore the unknown and the undiscovered, just as they are held to stagnation by those who gladly chant the clichés and pocket the cheques.

I wish to emphasise a crucial point: The criticism of a model is not, in any sense, dependent upon our providing an alternative model. We frequently hear the assertion that a standard model may well be faulty, but it's still the best we have. The implication is that before we are permitted to falsify a theory, we must devise and supply a better one. What nonsense. If a model is faulty, we do science — and the world — immense service by pointing it out. Asserting that there *has* to be a model, faulty or not, is another twist on model-dependent science. Frankly, I find that sort of reasoning quite illogical and a prime cause of the trouble we're in.

This brings us to the sticky matter of consensus. Ultimately, truth is by no means the product of agreement amongst a majority. In fact, it emerges more often than not from the statistical opposite of consensus. How many people might believe in a particular model has no bearing whatsoever on whether that model aligns with objective reality. I found it useful to assume at the outset that *all* belief is false, and eliminate it entirely from the investigative groundwork. Then, in a suitably sterile environment, we are free to unpick the layers of the hypo-stack to search for some thread of truth that we can build on. Authentic science is not a democracy, and truth belongs to none of us.

Once again, I find myself idealising. In practice, is truth ever revealed this way? Well yes, now that you mention it, it is indeed. We recall from chapter four the well-worn, much cited case of timid Polish heretic, Nicolaus Copernicus. On his deathbed, Copernicus, an officer of the Roman Catholic Church, revealed to his close friend Bishop Tiedemann Giese the cloistered manuscript of his epic book, *On the Revolutions of the Celestial Spheres*. The dying scholar secured an undertaking from Giese to have it published, despite the dire risks it implied for the unfortunate prelate. On those secret, dusty pages, Copernicus put forward his theory that the Sun, rather than the Earth, was the centre of the universe as they knew it. That flew right in the face of the prevailing official version of cosmology,

the one that ancient Greek philosopher Aristotle had articulated nearly two thousand years before, and which the
Roman Catholic Church had later endorsed into its sacred
doctrine. Copernican heliocentricity was, in a word, *heresy*.

Enter Italian physicist Galileo Galilei. We need first to
set the scene, and indulge in a brief sojourn with Galileo's contemporaries towards the end of the sixteenth
century — most notably the monk and mathematician
Giordano Bruno. Although he was sixteen years younger
than Bruno, Galileo moved in much the same circles in
Italy and knew him well. He would certainly have watched
Bruno's unfolding intrigue with great interest. Bruno was
an even more committed heretic than Galileo, so his fate
should have curtailed young Galileo's hazardous leanings,
but it didn't. The Inquisition in due course arrested the
defiant Bruno, brought him before a tribunal, charged him
with heresy and sedition, and forced him to endure a trial
that lasted seven years. They accused him of a list of crimes
that included holding opinions against the Catholic faith;
speaking against it; and believing and promoting a cosmology based upon the principle that the Sun was a mere star,
and that there were millions more like it in the universe.

> God is infinite, so His universe must be too. Thus is
> the excellence of God magnified and the greatness
> of His kingdom made manifest; He is glorified not
> in one, but in countless suns; not in a single earth, a
> single world, but in a thousand thousand, I say in an
> infinity of worlds.
>
> *Giordano Bruno, On the Infinite*
> *Universe and Worlds, 1584*

The tribunal found Giordano Bruno guilty on all counts. The cardinals admonished him to recant, but he refused, famously telling his judges, "*Maiori forsan cum timore sententiam in me fertis quam ego accipiam*" (Perhaps you pronounce this sentence against me with greater fear than I receive it). On February 17th, 1600, his warders dragged him to a popular Roman market square, tied him securely to a stake, put out his tongue "for his wicked words", and then slowly and horrifyingly burned him alive. They dumped his charred remains unceremoniously into the Tiber River, and in 1603, the cardinals declared all his works prohibited. The protracted public execution must have greatly concerned Galileo when he first turned a telescope to the night skies in 1610, and with his own eyes saw convincing evidence that both Copernicus and Bruno had after all been right in the gist of what they said.

> In my studies of astronomy and philosophy I hold this opinion about the universe, that the Sun remains fixed in the centre of the circle of heavenly bodies, without changing its place; and the Earth, turning upon itself, moves round the Sun.
>
> *Galileo Galilei, letter to Cristina di Lorena, grand duchess of Tuscany, 1615*

I have been judged vehemently suspect of heresy, that is, of having held and believed that the sun in the centre of the universe and immoveable, and that the earth is not at the centre of same, and that it does move. Wishing however, to remove from the minds of your Eminences and all faithful Christians this vehement suspicion reasonably conceived against me, I abjure with a sincere heart and unfeigned faith, I curse and detest the said errors and heresies, and generally all and every error, heresy, and sect contrary to the Holy Catholic Church.

the formal abjuration that Galileo Galilei
was forced to recite and sign, church of Santa
Maria sopra Minerva, 22 June 1633

Galileo's integrity and dedicated empiricism left him no options; he had to call it as he saw it, and despite the privations of house arrest and draconian censorship, he ultimately escaped with his life. He published his heresy in the cleverly presented *Dialogues Concerning Two New Sciences*, where a roguish interlocutor proposed the forbidden truths, leaving the author as a mere reporter of the conversation.

These brave heretics — so few that we count them on the fingers of one hand — overthrew a consensus outnumbering them by a million to one. The greater truth emerged not from mainstream political agreement or mass religious conviction. It came from observation of nature by a small number of despised and denigrated individuals. The vast and apparently divinely ordained paradigm had been decisively overturned by nothing more than the virtue of heresy.

I should like us to pause here for a moment and reflect on the sorry tale of Bruno and Galileo. Their responses to their rulers were quite different. Bruno stood steadfast and was executed. Galileo on the other hand publicly recanted his beliefs, but continued to publish them surreptitiously. His punishment was far less severe than poor Bruno's. Bruno was driven by faith; Galileo by pragmatism.

I know of no better comparison in history of the stark juxtaposition between selfless belief and selfish pragmatism, between moral self-flagellation and goal-orientated science. We want to side with Bruno because we see him as a martyr representing the cries of our moral conscience. The reality check comes when we consider what they each achieved. The greater good of mankind was served by Galileo's scientific pragmatism in this case, and Bruno's fate stands as an abiding illustration of the power of superstition over reason. Above all, this sorry tale gives us a measure of the welcome scepticism gets when it dares to cast a pall of doubt on the ruling paradigm.

Scepticism, even in our supposedly enlightened times, is often no more than lip service. Scholars remain fiercely (and unreasonably) loyal to the paradigm they have come to represent, whether by faith or education, or both. Let's take two examples. By far, most New Testament scholars are Christians. Many are tenured in Christian Bible colleges. They are subjectively committed *a priori* to a belief in the standard doctrinal inferences of the scriptures they are studying. They have no interest whatsoever in trying to falsify the model. Indeed, quite the contrary. They investigate scripture with the sole intention of fine-tuning their preconceptions.

By far the majority of Big Bang scholars are cosmologists. Most cosmologists are aligned with the standard model taught as gospel in those schools that brought them to their present positions, and that now pay them to promulgate the gospel. It is a vast, lumbering system designed specifically to ensure its own survival by pinning medals to the chests of its champions.

Let us be perfectly clear here: Science by standard model — whatever benefits it is alleged to bring — suppresses the vital organic scepticism upon which objective analysis critically depends.

If these ideas were taught on the basis that they *might* be true, or that they are just one possible explanation of the world about us, there would be no problem. But when we present these hypotheses — or even worse, hypo-stacks — to young minds and declare them indisputably true, the practice of science goes horribly wrong. Rendering an idea the sole and only permissible method for understanding the mysteries violates the principles of the scientific method, thereby reducing science to politics. The fact of the matter is that we don't *know* that Big Bang theory or Jesus's resurrection or the 9/11 conspiracy theory is factually correct. We simply believe it.

I'd like to explore the notions of *agency* and *doctrine*. They seem to me to be symbiotically related. In particular, we might examine the very interesting link between doctrine and indoctrination. Firstly, however, let us consider agency.

Religion is a sociological phenomenon that operates exclusively upon the practice of agency. We are told *about* God by agents *of* God, and our understanding of the theological philosophy of any particular branch of religion is obtained via the eyes of its agents. If God itself told us the truth of the matter, then all religions would be the same. That they are so astonishingly varied is due entirely to the effect of agency.

Thus, we get self-proclaimed agents of God. Examples are Jesus of Nazareth, Muhammed of Mecca, and

Ron Hubbard of Nebraska, who all asserted (according to the official texts of the religions operating in their names) that they had a privileged primary connection to a higher power, and moreover had been tasked by divine authority to explain the whole shebang to the rest of us. We can be reasonably certain that they existed as real people in the historical milieu in which they proclaimed their business, and we know from contemporary reports that they rose to prominence for their utterances. The preferred version of history would have us believe that the agents could see and know things from source that ordinary folk are not able to, and many of us accepted their implied or express divinity, particularly those who were there at the time to bathe in that charismatic ambience. Level one of the agency pyramid had thereby been achieved.

The next level in the stack is occupied by the disciples, the chosen few whose task it is to formulate a doctrine from the philosophy or musings shared by the primary agent, and this takes off like wildfire after his demise. Even Scientology, which was copiously described and defined in literature by Ron Hubbard himself, suffered the subsequent implementation of a set of rules that had no roots in the original Hubbard scriptures. What we now have is management by committee, and the ghost of the late messianic agent becomes a figurehead for their efforts.

The ethos, or, if you will, the spirit of the burgeoning cult comes from the first (human) member of the hierarchy. He sits at the top of the pyramid, and what he says is (as far as we can tell) almost always related to practical matters and how to conduct daily life under the prevailing sociopolitical conditions of the time. Jesus was in all likelihood rebelling against Roman occupation; Muhammed was a tribal warrior; Hubbard was an engineer, seemingly constructing an empire to satisfy his own needs, and in that I dare say he was quite different in motivation from Jesus, if not from Muhammed. We can't know the true motivation of any of them, and it's not really important. What happened next is crucial.

Jesus did not leave us with his own written word, which is a great pity for scholarly research; Muhammed gave us the Quran, but since he was illiterate, he dictated it to scribes. After their respective deaths, the surviving devotees followed slightly dissimilar methods because of this essential difference in literary reference, but the ultimate effect was the same. Nazarenes began variously and independently to write accounts of the message they wanted to pass on about Jesus, and the Muhammedans fell back upon the traditional tribal councils and priests to devise and implement the Sharia law that they felt Muhammed had for some odd reason left out of his revelations from God.

It is important for us to realise that neither Jesus nor Muhammed had actual input to the laws and rules that were authored and brought to bear on the movements organised in their names. The doctrines of Christianity and Islam were articulated by men after the icons had left the Earthly realm. They are both fundamentally just secular ideologies that emerged from the quasi-political chaos of the time. These political manifestos have been dressed up with deities and hypnotic repetitions and fantastic stories of miracles by second-tier agents to give us the narratives that we have today.

Religious organisations are enhanced in the public eye by good works; all major religions partake in hearts-and-minds strategies of charitable intervention in circumstances of human suffering, but in a complete audit of their affairs, charity soon reveals itself as a relatively minor part of their daily business. Most of religion's energy is spent ensuring that their flocks are motivated to worship and contribute to the coffers, and providing the infrastructure and personnel to efficiently receive those offerings. Christianity and Islam as they are practised today would, in my opinion, be utterly unrecognisable to Jesus and Muhammed.

Two things are important here: Firstly, the founding figures of Christianity and Islam are completely innocent of the horrors that were subsequently committed in their names. The psychopathic behaviour from time to time inflicted by Christians and Muslims on those who get in their way is spawned by the organising of their respective cults by people far removed from the person and the philosophy of their founder. Secondly, the doctrine that emerges from the philosophy of iconic religious figures is always the outcome of organising the church. The doctrine is not theological; it is a political manifest. Religion is the political expression of theology. Whatever philanthropic divinity we might feel inclined to award to the primary agent is quickly lost on those who try to step into his shoes. That's the harsh historical fact of the matter.

Thus we witness the conversion over time of a theological model into a political movement, with all that the term implies. Part of that implication is the method employed to ensure the fertility of their doctrine in the minds of generations to come. Without exception, religious methodology centrally involves indoctrination. The main business of any cult is indoctrination. It is the most important thing they do.

If we try to distil the essential difference between religion and science in an ideal world, it looks something like this: Religious faith can work only if it is held beyond doubt; properly faithful religionists do not doubt their version of the truth. Science, on the other hand, is validated by doubt; any and all hypotheses put forward must in principle be falsifiable, and be subjected to the searing crucible of institutional scepticism. The zealous religionist subjects his world view to intellectual challenge solely to strengthen his convictions. The zealous scientist, by contrast, ought to challenge his assertions in a sincere attempt to prove them wrong.

In this perfect world where all players take their parts with superhuman dedication, science and religion stand in precise opposition to each other. In a world where form is defined by spin, and where polarity provides equilibrium and symmetry, the classical roles played by religion and physics are a perfect fit. But something went wrong. Now we have an inversion of their prior positions, a confused anarchy where religionists are applying scientific scepticism to the tenets of their doctrine, and scientists are building their models upon articles of faith. Neither system can work properly if they abandon their essential polarity for an androgynous middle ground. How can we right this listing ship?

Every hypothesis should be greeted with scepticism. I mean this; every single one, no exceptions. The reason is simple enough: On what basis could we possibly qualify exceptions to the rule? The decision to declare a particular hypothesis above scepticism would have to be motivated by our preordained belief—in other words, we don't need to question it simply because we believe in it—and that is the very constraint we are trying so hard to expunge from our quest for objective knowledge. The shepherding effect of belief is universal, and determines where our enquiry would prefer to go. Having taken that warm, fuzzy direction, we invariably have our faculty for discrimination lulled into stupor. We find merit with new ground not because it matches the data but for no better reason than that it harmonises with our preconceptions.

> Most institutions demand unqualified faith; but the institution of science makes skepticism a virtue.
> *Robert King Merton, sociologist (1910–2003)*

To summarise: at universities, performance pressure makes faith in standard models indispensible; we are sent forth with canonised fundamentals and token, superficial scepticism. The places that thence entice our enquiry are comfort zones from which we can employ all our intelligence and powers of argument to perpetrate the received method of enquiry. Faith, by its very nature, does not encourage or even allow scepticism.

Belief suppresses our faculty for intelligent discrimination, and can powerfully influence our opinions. What's more, belief all but eliminates the need for scepticism. One of the clearest examples of this facet of belief comes from the Christian Bible. From the point of view of the believer, if there's a conflict between what the Bible says and the discoveries of science, it is science that must be wrong; scientists should revisit their assertions and correct them to align with scripture. However, from the scientist's perspective, it is the Biblical passages, or perhaps the orthodox interpretations of the Bible, that are mistaken. This opposition of opinion forms a long-standing impasse.

One of the major problems facing the secular scholar is establishing with sufficient precision and clarity just what the verses actually mean, and thus revealing for objective analysis what the author meant us to understand from them. Even for devout believers, this is no easy matter, hence the plethora of sometimes conflicting interpretations we are given by various religious analysts. We should study this matter very carefully. A wonderful opportunity to assess the effect of belief on our opinions lies in the differences between those faith-aligned meanings and the unadorned translation provided by secular historians.

Some Christian believers contend that scripture makes references to certain aspects of the world that would not have been obvious to ordinary folk at the time. If more recent scientific discoveries can be positively linked to ancient scriptural descriptions of the world, written at a time when the technological facilities to make such observations did not yet exist, it would be powerful support — proof even — that the prophets had privileged connections to God itself. Bible scholars have listed more than fifty such instances, and they are proudly put forward in evidence.

Several Christian websites make these assertions, so I have chosen one that is not exceptional — *inplainsight.org*, and the specific article "Scientific Facts in the Bible" by Carol Brooks. Applying everyday scepticism to Ms Brooks' interpretations soon reveals the profound effect that belief has on our ability to understand evidence. Consider the following:

> It is He that . . . stretches out the heavens as a curtain,
> and spreads them out as a tent to dwell in.
>
> *Isaiah 40:22*

This quote is said to be a revelation of the expanding space hypothesis of Big Bang theory. An objective reader would find no such meaning or evidence of deeper insight in this reading; it is simply a rustic philosopher's description of the celestial sphere as it appears to anyone who gazes at the night sky.

> When He imparted weight to the wind and meted out the waters by measure . . . .
>
> *Job 28:25*

The assumption that this quote makes a reference to atmospheric pressure is patently slanted. The phrase "weight to the wind" would far more likely refer to the mysterious invisible force exerted by the wind as perceived by a scientifically unsophisticated person of that era. There is no rational way to interpret how wind is felt as a description of atmospheric pressure.

> As the host of heaven cannot be numbered, nor the sand of the sea measured, so will I multiply the descendants of David My servant.
>
> *Jeremiah 33:22*

This quote, said to prove early knowledge of the vast number of stars in the universe, seems odder than the others. The overwhelming scale of our surroundings is hardly a scientific discovery. This is clearly an allegorical analogy, intended to imply how greatly David would multiply his progeny. Interpreting the cited text as an example of scientific insight is a great stretch.

> He sits enthroned above the circle of the earth, and
> its people are like grasshoppers.
>
> *Isaiah 40:22*

Brooks uses this passage to suggest that the Bible's authors knew that the Earth was a sphere. From any high point, however, an observer would perceive the horizon as a circle, or a series of arcs. This would have been the observation and the opinion of anyone at relatively high altitude, and demonstrates no scientific understanding of the world at all. Extrapolating this text to reach the conclusion that it describes a spherical Earth is again meaning imputed by pre-existing belief.

> Hast thou commanded the morning since thy days;
> and caused the dayspring to know his place; that it
> might take hold of the ends of the earth, that the
> wicked might be shaken out of it? It is turned as clay
> to the seal; and they stand as a Garment.
>
> *Job 38:12*

Leaving aside that "the ends of the Earth" contradicts the previous point about the Earth being a sphere (a sphere has no ends, but a disk has an edge), one would be hard pressed to find in this quote any explicit description of planetary rotation, as Ms Brooks suggests is the case. The term "dayspring" refers to sunrise, which would apply equally in a geocentric model of the Sun in orbit around a non-rotating Earth. The word "turned" does not indicate rotation in this context; it means "changed into." The concept of a rotating, spherical Earth is inadvertently debunked in its entirety by the quoted text, per this explanation from Ms Brooks: "*As soon as the sun is risen, its light will take hold of the ends of the earth in the sense that it touches all of the landscape.*" This explanation could apply only to a one-sided, flat Earth; the spherical Earth is lit by halves.

The list goes on and on, and in my view as an astrophysicist, does not make a single clear statement that indicates that the authors of the Bible's books had advanced knowledge of the actual cosmos. Indeed, independent study of the scriptures indicates quite the opposite. According to Moses, God seemed not to know even the most elementary features of the Solar System, and if God did know these things, was keeping them a close secret. It is not my intention here to prove the Bible wrong; merely to indicate that the ideology and doctrines that have been extracted from biblical scripture are shaped entirely by pre-existing bias. To impute prophetic knowledge of scientific discoveries that would be made many centuries hence is to expose inherent bias. To the best of my knowledge, there is not a scrap of legitimate science anywhere in the Bible, and it remains no more than a fabulous anthropological journal from antiquity. Faith in the divine does not need science, and should in my opinion be considerably more circumspect when summoning that sort of meaning from the scriptures.

The solution I propose to this quandary is scientific pragmatism, an outcomes-based system of information engineering. It seems painfully clear that the only sensible way forward in learning about nature is to begin by sterilis-ing our instruments and our laboratories, rendering them clear of contamination by belief. This necessarily requires the stringent application of eye-watering doubt — recall that Richard Feynman famously said that *"sScience is the culture of doubt"* — and we shall have to develop the skills to do this properly. We don't want to put the baby out with the bathwater.

Evaluating models can be both tricky and tiresome. I often wonder if it's worth the effort. Models are there ostensibly to make our enquiry more efficient, and if they were properly constructed, they would indeed leapfrog us along the path of our investigation. If models were con-structed from the ground up in layers of empirically tested laws rather than untested hypotheses, they would still be open to human error, but at a far more acceptable level. My approach is to start at the bottom of the stack, to where we have those beliefs — call them assumptions, axioms, received wisdom, whatever — upon which the model was constructed. I examine those first to see if they have the basis of scientific integrity.

I concede that this is going to be a judgement call, but hopefully it will be the last vestige of subjectivity before I tackle the theoretical construct with what I hope will be merciless empirical honesty. If the primary assumptions reflect a plausible take on the real world in which it is to operate, I tackle the next layer in the stack, proceeding systematically to test each stratum of the model until I either find one that fails, or I reach the top.

Here we must emphasise a matter of great importance: Each and every tenet of the theoretical structure must be testable, and if it is testable, it is in principle falsifiable. If it passes the test, our confidence goes up; if it fails, we either reject it outright, or modify it to rectify the point of failure. There is a crucial caveat at this stage of the verification of a model — we test a stratum only so that it can successfully pass us on to the next level. We should at all costs avoid testing it against the topmost layer of the stack. That layer is the logical apex of the model, its conclusion; if we adjust troublesome tenets along the way to contrive a fit with the model's stated conclusion, we are practicing politics, not science. Treating elements of a theoretical construct in that way earns them the colloquial names "tuning knobs" or "fudge factors" because it bends the facts to achieve a desired outcome. In my book, that is plainly unethical, but be that as it may, it's clearly not a method that produces reliable, practicable outcomes.

The question of course is exactly *how* do we test a theory or any of its subsets? That's easy: There is one way — and one way only — to test a theory, and that's against reality. We cannot verify a model by testing it against itself mathematically (by establishing internal consistency or validating the syntax) or against another model. We cannot test it philosophically. We cannot test it in our imaginations; testing the logic tests only the logic. If we're seeking real-world solutions to real-world problems, then we put it by some means into the crucible of nature and see if it works there.

If it produces the predicted results consistently and unambiguously in our physical environment, then it's time for applause, not before. No hocus-pocus.

Please note that when I say *test against reality*, I mean test against *real* reality, in other words, the here and now. Much as I detest arguing by means of word manipulation, I feel compelled to make this point. It is particularly relevant to scholars of history. I have coined a mantra in this regard — the evidence for faith is yet more faith.

Christian apologists busy themselves making the case for intellectual, ostensibly scientific Christianity. The crux of their argument rests upon the premise that the resurrection of Jesus, as depicted in the New Testament, is testable and therefore falsifiable. Their contention consequent to this premise is that biblical resurrection can be considered a matter of pure science validating the central doctrine of Christianity, rather than a study of fable in ancient literature. Testing a premise from historical accounts, using purported eyewitness testimony, is dubious at best, completely ineffectual at worst. We would have to make a subjective call on the reliability of the account, and that brings to bear what we think the motivation of the author was. Furthermore, we must decide if he relies on the accounts of devoted disciples, in which case we cannot ignore the dialogic process.

In assessing the physics of a miracle, we must necessarily bring our instruments to bear upon the event itself, and not rely solely on subjective accounts from the mists of history. No historian, in the words of Max Müller, *"can ever pretend to do more than to show us what a man or a fact seemed to be to him or to the authorities whom he has to follow, and not what he or it actually was."* I would add that eyewitness accounts describe a scene *as it is remembered by the witness*, and it is indisputable that memory adds subjective hues to the recall. Unless the miracle is reproducible for analysis in the here and now, we cannot pronounce on it in terms of science. It remains just a belief, supported by those who feel inclined to accept it.

My aim, therefore, is to provide a method whereby one can build a new world view. We want to be sceptical, yes, but it should be pragmatic scepticism. I have no doubt that Big Bang theory will perish, and that another imaginative structure will usurp its throne. Unfortunately, belief systems come with a whole lot of baggage, and we have to implode the edifice carefully. Before we can make a proper start to creating a new model, we have to clear the debris of the old one. That means starting virtually from scratch, I'm afraid. It requires a critical mind and deep interrogation of the bottom layers in the hypo-stack. We must tackle the roots, not the leaves.

Why? Well, if the model is after all an incorrect description of reality — and that's what our scepticism seeks to establish — then we don't want to be distracted arguing about all the little things that branch out at every opportunity. We could end up spending valuable years and a great deal of anguish debating whether Bayesian or Monte Carlo analysis returns the best picture of the dawn of creation in the haze of the cosmic microwave background radiation, or sweating endless hours of bloody calculus over the Hubble Constant's projected rate of universal expansion. At the end of the day, all those esoteric constructs become completely irrelevant if the foundations of the standard model of cosmology are invalid. We would be arguing about smoke and mirrors. The three-way bet Stephen Hawking made with Kip Thorne and John Preskill in 1977 is another example. After thirty years spent trying to figure out whether information would be lost in passing the event horizon of a black hole, Hawking admitted he'd been wrong and paid up. The debate was all the more ludicrous because black holes have never been verified independently of the model. They are merely treetop artefacts in a vast hypo-stack. The devil is in the details, and those details form the quicksand that suffocates the life out of heretics.

Belief predates the Internet by untold millennia, but has it ever found a new friend in the World Wide Web! The information revolution brought immeasurable improvement to the dissemination of information and to the enlightenment of Mammon. But it has a dark side. It is even more proficient in spreading misinformation and giving sinister propaganda a veneer of respectability. Absolutely anyone can publicise their five pence' worth to a vast international audience, and there are countless cyber mastheads ready and willing to fly your particular pennant. One of the most widely used of these is the ubiquitous, universally referenced Wikipedia.

Wikipedia is an online compendium of knowledge written by the general cyber public. It has moderators and a set of basic rules lending it the appearance at least of scholarliness. It's a good idea, but the danger exists that it provides a ready platform for propaganda. Personal bias comes out of the woodwork, and sometimes Wikipedia (and even more so, its cheeky clone RationalWiki) is just a soapbox for disgruntled individuals with an axe to grind. There is even less objective balance in the articles than in mainstream science, and we've seen already how bad that is. That Wikipedia has become the world's most widely used general reference source is alarming but inevitable; we can only hope that it will be used prudently.

There is another aspect to scepticism that concerns us here: Conspiracy theories are scepticism gone mad. Sometimes the scepticism itself becomes the primary motivation for accepting a particular theory. This approach appeals particularly to the rebellious idealist, who might view himself as a "professional undresser of public hoaxes and silent conspiracies", for want of a more fitting description. In terms of approaching the truth, the outcome foisted upon us by conspiracists is easily as bad as that achieved by theological dogma. The closet iconoclast who lies concealed in some of us comes out snarling, teeth bared, when there's even a sniff of conspiracy in global events. Instead of being just a method of enquiry, albeit a very important one, scepticism is raised to the altar and worshipped. It takes on a life of its own, and becomes a god we pray to.

A final word about iconoclasts: desire to overturn the orthodoxy is quite common, but not because it's *wrong*. People who zealously pursue the goal of shifting the paradigm do it more often than not because they want to enshrine their own preferred model. In other words, it is a model-dependent action.

There is arguably nothing that suppresses healthy scepticism as much as canonised authority. Much of what we believe is derived from the appeal of authority. There are esteemed personalities in our hierarchy of references that take on exalted status in our eyes, and with whom we are impressed that they become infallibly correct from our personal point of view. Usually, these figureheads of accepted authority are human, but there is also a significant proportion of institutional authority. Thus, we have the Roman Catholic Church, NASA, Greenpeace, the 9/11 Truth movement, the UN's Intergovernmental Panel on Climate Change, and The National Geographic Society seen as purveyors of undiluted truth by those who choose to submit to their authority. We tend to accept their messages without question. The crucial aspect of the appeal of authority is the subjective nature of our choice of role model in the first place.

Those who task themselves with developing and promoting belief systems invariably invoke authority — sometimes quite maliciously — and it works a treat in avoiding sceptical analysis. Thus we hear assertions that three hundred architects prove the official 9/11 story wrong, that God inspired the Bible, and that Lance Armstrong led the campaign against doping in sport.

Our ability to hold rational discourse that can lead to fresh discovery and the progress of our understanding is sometimes limited by our choice of authority. I have had the experience of attempting to engage with well-meaning religious agents who regularly come knocking at my door. I bear them no ill will, and they mean me no harm, so at the outset we're on good terms. But as far as meaningful discussion goes, we quickly hit an impasse that's difficult to overcome. Their chosen authority, upon which their entire doctrine is based, is the Christian Bible. In seeking some possible interface with them, I have tried declaring my considered opinion: The Bible is just a mixture of myth, fable, genealogy, and political messages aimed specifically at a primitive social milieu that existed thousands of years ago. I do not believe that it is the infallible, divinely inspired, sovereign word of God that my uninvited guests seemed to think it was. So my point of departure was to initiate debate on the authenticity of the Bible as an authority on matters of universal truth.

We were immediately stymied. We simply cannot logically approach the issue of the Bible's veracity by quoting from the Bible. Despite the considerable momentum that their faith gave them, my guests and I could not proceed, and I had to politely accept their gift of religious tracts, bid them adieu, and restore my day to its prior equilibrium. These people exhibit a simple faith that I'm inclined to admire for its rustic charm, and quite honestly, I prefer it to the intellectualisations brought to the table by Christian apologists. I have engaged with them too, but after some considerable effort, I surrendered and went my way. I don't doubt that they would read this capitulation on my part as some sort of victory, and I don't mind at all. It's part of my ongoing education in sociology, and helps me to understand the dogmas of science. The principles are the same.

If we accept a theoretical model as our ultimate authority, we expose an Achilles' heel. All models are founded upon assumptions and belief, and ideological momentum dictates that we are naturally inclined to accept as evidence certain utterances without the need to thoroughly check them for veracity and ambiguity. Even the methods we use to "test" (read, *confirm*) our arguments, and indeed also the methodology employed in cited experiments, are converted by the belief filter to more easily digestible fodder. I have referred to this bolting of aligned opinions and summary rejection of opposing ideals as *unseemly haste*. Our bias is exposed by speed.

Once again, let's hark back to the example being set in the climate change debate. What is the general public to make of all hype surrounding climate? They don't have access to the raw data, and even if they did, they wouldn't know how to extract something useful from what would appear to them to be gibberish. The man in the street is left at the mercy of spin doctors. This is a very real problem for science, and calls into question the value of scientific models as a social shepherd. Who are we to believe? We don't even know whether scientists actually agree on all the gumph being spouted through the media. We are told they do, but *do* they? It's very difficult to get to the truth of the matter. The most compelling case is the one that best utilises the hypnotic effect of electronic media, and ultimately comes down to a public relations exercise for various political groups, including — significantly — NGOs. Sceptics will take the trouble to research opposing viewpoints, but even there, information is to some extent preselected. Google searches more often than not return the glamorous, heavily hit web pages first, so once again the poor citizen is dazzled by spin, from both sides.

A reasonably objective investigation should at least demonstrate that there are copious and persuasive arguments from both sides, and make it clear that Joe Public is left sucking the hind tit when it comes to finding out what's really going on. It should be obvious that we can't know for certain just who, if anyone, is telling the truth.

My question to the world then is this: How come, given the great uncertainty in the information we use to make decisions on these matters, we nevertheless still take sides and believe with gritted teeth one side or the other? Where does the power of that belief come from?

It's not from science; that much is certain.

I had many role models, mentors, and patrons who put up with my nonsense in the hope, I suppose, of getting something meaningful out of me before it was too late. Three of those were really famous — Sir Patrick Moore, Steven Weinberg, and Richard P Feynman. Weinberg and Feynman were Nobel Laureates, and Moore held seven honorary doctorates. Of the three, however, it was Feynman who had the gift of concise precis. He had this to say about authority: "*Science is the belief in the ignorance of experts.*"

Prof Feynman said "*science is the belief,*" *and* he could have left it there, really. Science, however purely it may start upon an investigation, ends up as belief. And when it *commences* from a pre-existing belief, it becomes a glorious hypo-stack, defying the rational wind in a tenuous floppy structure that stands up purely because it is indignant. The whole, massive, convoluted, arcane, magical Big Bang cosmology exists for no other reason than that some oratorially gifted individuals believed in Einstein's then-unproven general relativity theory with such unwavering conviction that they would dedicate their lives and promotional talents to nothing else. Eddington, Le Maître, Gamow, Peebles, and Dicke — top-class men, every single one of them — evangelised general relativity–based cosmology so successfully that it has become an icon of dictatorship.

The entire chain of succession is subverted to the canons of Big Bang theory and the specific methodology that spawned it in the first place. We are taught from our very first nascent inquisitiveness that the preferred belief is an axiom, and we are trained in that style of enquiry and expression so arduously that we are equipped upon graduation to do no other thing. No self-respecting university would dream of giving a doctorate in physics to someone who is not an absolute master of mathematics, and no postgraduate qualification in cosmology dares to wander from the narrow confines of the Big Bang footpath.

Another distressing source of unquestioned authority is in cited experiments. There is a tendency to believe that experiments are as infallible as the Pope to those who believe such things. This is not the case. Experiments are open to a wide range of deficiencies and aberrations, from skewed initial assumptions, set-up and equipment limitations, biased selection of effects, and most importantly to us here, to shamefully wild interpretation of results. The peer-review system, such as it is, does little more than encourage authors to skew results.

Our scepticism must apply first and foremost to model-dependent science. The dead giveaway is research that declares the conclusion before it has even begun to gather data, allowing the implication that the model verifies itself. I understand why scientists behave this way, but I am at a complete loss to suggest a solution to the problem. In writing out a proposal for a research grant, even one that is supposedly non-commercial — perhaps applying to the head of department at a university for project funds — one simply *has* to include hooks to catch and persuade the potential patron, and that invariably includes the expected, politically correct outcome.

Of course, the very same rules apply to our own models. We are so often utterly seduced by the fine, elegant detail of our own belief when all the while the foundations are clay. Hence, having established that the currently popular model is fundamentally flawed, we need to clear it away from our minds and telescopes, and get back to basics. It's rather like slashing our way through a bramble patch; we shall no doubt be left bleeding before the cleansing process is complete.

What a difficult obstacle this obsession with imagined models is to overcome. We believe things largely because we like to believe them. We take great satisfaction from immersing ourselves in beliefs. It's one of the stubborn difficulties I face in this thesis; asking a believer to surrender his faith is like expecting an addict to give up heroin. But it has to be done.

We tend to believe because we are predisposed to do so. It is a manifestation of instinctive bias. It is as well to bear in mind that *all* belief is counterproductive to science, no matter how dearly we love it; our immediate task, therefore, is to identify and nullify the belief filter on our investigative spectacles. We need to allow a natural, uncontrived scepticism to clear the crime scene of emotion. We have a job of work to do here.

Scientific pragmatism depends critically upon both our innate exploratory drive and the evolution of our knowledge base, generation after generation. In 1676, Sir Isaac Newton, the founder of scientific pragmatism and father of classical, cause-and-effect mechanics, famously wrote to his rival Robert Hooke (concerning the pioneering work of French mathematician René Descartes):

> What Des-Cartes did was a good step. You have
> added much several ways, & especially in taking
> ye colours of thin plates into philosophical consid-
> eration. *If I have seen further it is by standing on ye*
> *sholders of Giants.*

Ironically, the cranky Newton soon lost his patience with
Hooke, and after a spat in which Hooke criticised some
of Newton's concepts in optics (Hooke was a pioneer of
the microscope), Newton withdrew from all further public debate and the two remained bitter enemies until they
were finally separated by death. The principle, however,
remains clear: Our individual contributions are to the species, not to ourselves. We make contributions to the future
like bytes of information make up a data stream. We live for
the briefest of moments, and then we die, leaving behind a
vague mark, like an exposed foothold that was not as clear
before we kicked some dirt away. Each byte stands upon
the head of the one before, and gives a leg-up to the one
that follows. On the paltry human scale that defines us as
people, our individual achievements are greatly significant,
but what remains especially important at the end is not
the quantum; it is the big picture to which the quantum
adds a flash of colour that lives on. At some higher level
that frame is so big, so all-encompassing that it lives forever.
And that, I suppose, is the meaning of life.

> The time will come when diligent research over long
> periods will bring to light things that now lie hid-
> den. A single life time, even though entirely devoted
> to research, would not be enough for the investiga-

tion of so vast a subject. And so this knowledge will be unfolded through long successive ages. There will come a time when our descendants will be amazed that we did not know things that are so plain to them. Many discoveries are reserved for ages still to come, when memory of us will have been effaced. Our universe is a sorry little affair unless it has in it something for every age to investigate. Nature does not reveal her mysteries once and for all.

Seneca, Natural Questions, *book 7, around the first century* AD

When I speak of pragmatism, I am not eliminating the romance of spirituality. The unknown is ever present, a cloak about the meagre body of certain knowledge. We should always allow ourselves the freedom to peek into those shadowy spaces, and to conjure up mental images of what we think the dark caverns of the cosmos and the secret madness of atoms might be hiding from us. Science expresses a natural, healthy hunger for knowledge and enlightenment, and has its place in our philosophy of the world. We become charlatans and scoundrels only when and if we speak of those imagined things with unwavering certainty, as if our minds have somehow made them real. What lies beyond the horizon of my own perception and understanding is not yet mine to employ, and may never be; at least, I can reasonably expect to command no more than the smallest piece of it. We are tinkers and tailors and candlestick makers, not masters of the universe.

What of the supernatural? Of course there are forces and dynamics yet to be described by science. Phenomena exist abundantly that current knowledge cannot adequately or surely explain. That's a given. But that's not the problem. The problem arises when people claim knowledge and understanding of supernatural events, often things which are imaginary anyway.

Science has no business with complete answers, and very little, if anything, to do with questions on a scale greater than we can reliably measure. That is the province of some or other flavour of philosophy. Science is the ongoing construction of bits and pieces, of discrete quanta in an endless patchwork quilt. The ultimate value of physics to the human tribe is expressed by engineers solving problems, not magi dealing cards.

What astonishes me endlessly is that we should need to be told that. It really ought to be quite obvious, and not in the least bit worth mentioning. For all our vast banks of knowledge, have we no wisdom at all?

Reality is that which, when you stop believing in it, doesn't go away.

PHILIP K. DICK

6

A CONSPIRACY OF THEORIES

The great spin doctor's revival show

IN THE PRECEDING CHAPTERS, we set the tone for an enquiry into the dizzying maze of belief. It hasn't been easy. We are soaked in the stuff. We humans positively reek of belief. I don't know, as you and I lounge in our subjective sandpit, if we could ever have a sensible discussion about objectivity, but I am surely going to try. So fasten your seat belt please....

Let us review, very briefly, what we have covered so far: Belief is an instinctive, subjective organisation of information coming at us from the natural world; none of us is free from belief; it separates us from pristine truth; we need to find a way to minimise its impact on our collective knowledge base. Before we proceed, I think it would be a jolly good idea to look at some examples of how belief has tainted the sacred cows of scientific endeavour.

Author Len Deighton once wrote, *"Experience is a method of endorsing prejudice."* Dominant models rule our

$$dE = \frac{R}{g}\, dA + \Omega\, dJ + \Phi\, dQ$$

o me, the notion of mathematical exclusivity is utterly absurd. It locks science into a modus that protects the fundamentals from independent investigators, no matter how deep their non-mathematical knowledge may be. In effect, reality is not defined by mathematics per se, but by our ability with the language. Reality in the scheme becomes truly user-defined and observer-dependent.

lives, and in doing so illustrate several facets of belief in practice — ideological momentum,[1] the dialogic process,[2] and what I call *faith drag*,[3] the moralistic clinging to the ashes of a defunct idea. This is not a critique of faith *per se*, merely an illustration, by example, of how easily it can lead one astray.

When Hawking gave up on black holes, it was momentous[4]. So too was Peter Woit's denial of string theory[5]. But their flocks would not deny it. They were captured by belief. *"What a weak barrier truth is when it stands in the way of an hypothesis,"* said Mary Wollstonecroft Shelley. Indeed.

The multifarious roles that belief systems play in our lives was put into hilarious perspective in the hit TV series

---

1 Ideological momentum: The impetus of collective opinion; the tendency for supportive results to emerge and grow artificially from prior consensus or authority; also called "the snowball effect"; a synthetic trend in which we impute meaning in things just because we want meaning to be there for whatever deeply held reason, and then take that meaning forward even when it has been objectively falsified.

2 Dialogic Process: The predisposition of devoted disciples to see miracles. (Max Muller).

3 Faith drag, aka ideological inertia: a consequence of the power of belief over reason: The tendency of reason to trail belief; articles of faith that remain popularly in place despite the objective overturning of previously accepted supporting evidence; the time lag between a paradigm shift in science and a modification of belief to accommodate it.

4 S. W. Hawking, "Information Preservation and Weather Forecasting for black holes (date TK) doi: arxiv: 1401.5761.

5 Peter Woit, *Not Even Wrong: The Failure of String Theory and the Search for Unity in Physical Law* (New York: Basic Books, 2006).

The Big Bang Theory.[6] The scene takes place in the lounge of the flat theoretical physicist Dr Sheldon Cooper shares with experimental physicist Dr Leonard Hofstadter. Leonard is making out on the sofa with his new girlfriend, Dr Leslie Winkle, another theoretical physicist. Sheldon interrupts them, and a side-splitting kerfuffle ensues about the relative merits of string theory (promoted by Sheldon) and loop quantum gravity (of which Leslie is a great fan). It plays out like this:

> **Sheldon** (*in response to Leslie's outburst about loop quantum gravity*): I'm listening. Amuse me.
>
> **Leslie**: Okay, for one thing, we expect quantum space-time to manifest itself as minute differences in the speed of light for different colours ...
>
> **Sheldon**: Balderdash! Matter clearly consists of tiny strings.
>
> **Leslie** (*turning indignantly to Leonard*): Are you going to let him talk to me like that?
>
> **Leonard**: Okay, well, there's a lot of merit in both theories ...
>
> **Leslie** (*raising her voice*): No, there's NOT! Only loop quantum gravity calculates the entropy of black holes!
>
> **Sheldon**: (*snort of derision*)

---

6 *The Big Bang Theory*: TV comedy series, created by Chuck Lorre and Bill Prady. The three characters mentioned here were played by Jim Parsons (Sheldon), Johnny Galecki (Leonard), and Sara Gilbert (Leslie) respectively.

Leslie *(to Leonard)*: You agree with me, right? Loop quantum gravity *is* the future of physics!"

Leonard: Sorry, Leslie, I guess I prefer my space stringy and not loopy.

Leslie *(exasperated)*: FINE! I'm glad I found out the truth about you before this went any further!

Leonard: Truth? What truth? We're talking about untested hypotheses. Look, it's no big deal ...

Leslie: Oh, it isn't? Really? Tell me Leonard, how will we raise the children?

Leonard: I guess we wait until they're old enough and let them choose their theories ...

Leslie *(storming out)*: You can't let them choose, Leonard! They're CHILDREN!

No wonder *The Big Bang Theory* is my favourite television series, despite a name that sticks in my craw. The dialogue almost casually hits the nerve of human frailty, episode after episode. Genius!

Belief invariably hardens when one is exposed to propaganda that disseminates an idea, provided of course that the idea being put forward harmonises with one's predisposition. Once belief takes control, the evidence presented is subjectively censored without due diligence, and doctrinal filters ensure that nothing contrary is granted validity. The dogma remains safe. My mother would often tell me, *"Hilton, you can argue yourself into anything."* How right she was. The pursuit of objectivity in science eventually became a passion for me (and I reflect on how dangerous that can be). It has involved trying to put myself forward as some kind of professional agnostic, forever claiming that we can't know absolutely, and that belief does not make our opinions divine.

I don't think anyone could have fairly predicted just how enormous and far-reaching the effects of instant global communication would become, but the Internet is now one of the great wonders to emerge from the twentieth century. The World Wide Web provides effective channels for the global spread of ideas and information that might otherwise never have gone much further than the writer's desk. Along with the opening up of thoughts and ideals and discoveries, the Web also provides unprecedented opportunities for commerce and revenue. But more startling than any of its more glamorous achievements has been the incredibly efficient platform the Internet has turned out to be for the propagation of fraud and deception.

The need to proselytise is one of the most annoying aspects of belief-driven behaviour. We develop a belief, become proud of it and what it says about us, and then set about projecting our garnished self-image upon the hapless folk who fall into the sweep of our radar. The advent of mass-communication media riding on the Internet makes the task of evangelising our opinions that much easier. The World Wide Web, for all its magnificence, has a darker side.

A very interesting rule has emerged from the anarchy of Internet discussions. In 1990, while the pubescent World Wide Web was still rubbing the sleep from its eyes, a fellow named Mike Godwin identified a trend. It has since become known as *Godwin's law*, and he states it thus: "*As an online discussion grows longer, the probability of a comparison involving Nazis or Hitler approaches one.*"

In plain language, Godwin says that any Internet discussion thread, given enough time and no matter what it's about, invariably introduces a reference to Hitler or the Nazis. In 2012, Godwin's law became an entry in the Oxford English Dictionary.

What has this to do with what we are discussing here? Quite a lot, actually. As it became more widely used in Internet forums, Godwin's law took on a slightly different meaning. It is nowadays taken to indicate that the blogger invoking Hitler has run out of authentic arguments, and that the time has come to close the thread. References to Hitler in any arbitrary context are considered overtly inappropriate, often called *"playing the Hitler card."* Hitler is a powerful metaphor, and should be used sparingly in civilised discussion; sadly, online discussions are seldom civilised. What Godwin's law illustrates for me is how easily people support their beliefs by loose analogy. Arguments are rarely, if ever, really supported by mentioning Hitler, and it shows a measure of desperation, in my opinion. It's a form of fibbing, a blight on our quest for truth, but it remains nevertheless a pertinent sign of the times.

Up there on the Web, our cyber persona usurps our real blemished self, and we magically become younger, sexier, and infinitely cleverer. It's rather like being drunk, with the ghastly caveat that we are at the same time quite untouchable. We can rant and froth and insult, and not a soul can punch us in the face. From the protected ivory tower of Internet platforms, we can spew and spam with impunity. And that brings us to another fascinating nuance of beliefiosity: Our knee-jerk participation in the dark art of *forwarding.*

Here I am in grave danger of succumbing to my own passion. I detest the exponentially exploding messages that clog our cyber conduits, almost as much as I abhor conspiracy theories and cruelty. It seems to me that they somehow offend my personal morality, and therefore immediately volunteer themselves as prime candidates for the analytical microscope being deployed in this book. The very existence of verification sites like *Snopes* and *Hoax-Slayer*, and the thousand upon thousand pages of evidence they present, bear testimony to just how far this scourge has reached.

What concerns us as behavioural scientists is not so much the motivation of the shadowy authors of Internet spam (although that is interesting in itself), but the reasons why we so impulsively hit the forward button. If we did not pass electronic chain letters on to our friends, one of the great plagues of the twenty-first century would simply die out. It seems to me that we are belief automatons.

As with all belief, the overwhelming majority of electronically forwarded broadcasts (in effect, chain letters) are hoaxes, and even worse, frauds. They range from mildly misleading to downright dangerous, from Tweets to BBM broadcasts to lavishly illustrated emails. As the world's most famous humanitarian Nelson Mandela lay in his hospital, kept with us still by life-support machines, the Tweets came flooding in pronouncing him by some privileged insight or prophetic ability already dead. The Tweets were picked up on media web pages, where they gained the respectability of a masthead and photographs, and before we knew it, the lies were going viral on Facebook and Windows Mail. If those messages keep going out daily, then it stands to reason that sooner or later they will coincide with the truth, and the false prophets will no doubt be canonised by their disciples.

We need to be careful. It's all too easy for us to become a monkey on the back of organised religion, but that would be missing the point rather badly. Religion, by my rustic definition, is a philosophical framework in which one can respectably claim the absurd. In my view, that gives it a charming honesty that overshadows the inherent irrationality of proclaiming knowledge of a realm governed by terrifyingly omnipotent, largely grumpy deities. We, the enlightened, freethinking readers of a book like this, may well be more interested in objectivity's yin than in religion's yang, but they are both important; like conservative and liberal in political sociology, they form an essential polarity, unavoidably part of the pairings that anchor our understanding of the world. Belief, let me say it again, is ubiquitous and impartial; it affects all of us in more or less equal measure. I'd like to illustrate this disquieting truth by looking past the ceremonial cloaks of some famous secular theories. Before we get down to specifics, let us digress just a tad to get a more microscopic handle on the social form of belief when it organises as a survival mechanism.

The buy-in to the most influential beliefs of our time has been lubricated and reinforced by an attitude best described as righteous indignation. It has to do with the perception of exclusive, privileged insight. We are stimulated by the idea that we have the vision to see past the veil of stupidity that smothers global opinions other than our own, and we consequently claim for ourselves the victory of truth. There is almost always some hint at conspiracy,

which we, the moral victors, have identified in the war we
wage on behalf of humanity.

Believers in man-made global warming see capitalism
as the global ogre, and they bravely face up to that particular threat in the costume of David before the awful Goliath.
Believers in 9/11 conspiracy latch onto the uttering of those
claiming to have an inside track on what actually bombed
the WTC, be it the US government, Jews, aliens, whatever.
Believers in alternative medicine decry the sinister choke-
hold that conventional medicine has on research and
clinical practice. Deniers of the Apollo landings see NASA
as an agency of the Illuminati. There is broad commonality
between these revolutionary believers. All see the promotion of their belief as a duty to mankind. All manufacture
evidence in support. All believe they hold the moral high
ground. All pay homage to the prophets of their belief,
and even more earnestly vilify those who oppose them.
All defend their positions with righteous indignation. It
is thus supremely ironical that those sucked into conspiracy theories at whatever level have in fact been duped into
believing that they are being duped.

There are things — great big cloudy things — so compelling to contemplate that we easily consider them vital
to the survival of our species. They are not, as it turns
out, but that we make them so. Theoretical physicists
spend their whole careers trying to model the entire universe, when it should be clear to common sense that such
an achievement, in the unlikely event that it could be
properly framed, would be quite impossible to test unambiguously against reality. Bertrand Russell pondered upon
his navel with such dedication that he produced, together

with mathematical idealist Alfred North Whitehead, the densely abstruse volume *Principia Mathematica* (what persuaded them to mimic the title of Isaac Newton's classic, I shall never know). It was an attempt to ground mathematics, such as the art had become, in logic; as far as I can tell, it failed to achieve that goal.

I am the first to admit that I don't quite get the gist of Russell's magnum opus, because mathematics at its roots and in the glory days of Euclid was simply a symbolic expression of logic, a clever way to derive quantities by recognising and simplifying patterns and relationships. That Russell and Whitehead should have produced a Britannica of philosophical gymnastics in order to *attempt* to relate mathematics to logic should immediately inform us that what they were dealing with was beyond the bound of pure mathematics, and had entered another, altogether more arcane realm. Call it what you will, mathematical syntax that is subverted and manipulated so that it can frame philosophical arguments is no longer mathematics. It is metamathematics.

The mathematical conception of the universe depends strictly upon one's skill and ability in mathematical techniques. The implication is that without the requisite fluency and understanding of mathematics, one is barred from forming a realistic conception of the world about us. It is shocking that these people, whose sole qualification for their position of power is advanced knowledge of an arcane, esoteric symbolic language that few in the world can understand, elevate themselves to the podium of all science. They become self-appointed, self-regulating high priests, immune to external challenge. Unless we are completely fluent in their chosen language (whether it is Sanskrit or Latin or Ancient Hebrew or hieroglyphics or differential geometry), we are denied access to real understanding. *They* decide. No one else.

I find the notion of mathematical exclusivity absurd. It locks science into a modus that protects the fundamentals from independent investigators, no matter how deep their non-mathematical knowledge may be. In effect, reality is not defined by mathematics *per se*, but by our ability with the language. Reality in that scheme becomes truly user-defined and observer-dependent. This is totally unacceptable to me.

The notion of black holes[7] is one of the clearest examples of this type of thinking in action. My own analysis of the black hole model suggests that it is not only completely absurd to a rational mind, but also mathematically untenable. In their haste to make magic, theorists building the model have made some fundamental errors in the formal flow of the equations they derive; their theory gains solutions where none truly exist. Faith drag ignores the errors. Now that the magi have mastered the trick, they simply cannot present their show without it.

My point is this: It's not so much *what* they were imagining that was the problem as the *way* they were doing it, and

---

7 Cosmological black holes are controversial theoretical constructs emanating from Einstein's general relativity theory. They are said to be so dense that their gravitation does not allow even light to escape, and consequently they cannot be directly seen. However, even indirect observations (like a silhouette or spherical light sink) have never been achieved. I must emphasise here that I do not know that black holes exist, or that they do not exist. Let's just say that I have not been convinced by the evidence.

ultimately, by what means they confirmed for themselves that their musings were indubitably true and real. There are two books to which I devoted special energy in a quest to find what made them so compelling to their followers: Russell and Whitehead's aforementioned *Principia Mathematica*, and Moses *et al*'s Christian Bible. In both cases I failed miserably, yet in an unexpected way, I garnered great profit from my labours. The means of expression were in both cases frustratingly obscure, and this was the key. It became clear to me that the meanings taken from those books (meanings which, it must be said, vary considerably amongst scholars) depend almost entirely upon the belief structures of the readers at the outset. This was, if you'll pardon the pun, a godsend, and led ultimately to the book you're reading now. The question I had to ask myself was the $64,000 question that frames the ultimate chapter of this work: What can be done about it?

In a nutshell, I concluded that while we ought not to constrain the conclusions that investigators reach after considering the data, we can and should improve considerably on the method employed to collect and present the primary evidence.

Whenever one buys into someone's theory or model, it is inevitable that a degree of hero worship creeps in. The author of the theory is in effect canonised, and becomes a preferred, infallible authority. Glazed adulation eventually forms a defensive perimeter that resists any form of critical analysis or falsification. I'm sure we all have friends or acquaintances who present these symptoms. The canonisation of an individual transforms the acolyte's thinking in a substantial way, with the result that in a surprisingly short time, theory is converted into full-blown doctrine.

Cults always form in the ambience of a particularly charismatic central character. The charisma exuded by cult leaders is not necessarily of the centre-stage, showbiz variety. In fact, it is very seldom overt. It really is an extraordinary talent, granting them the ability to completely remove rational filters from the minds of those who follow them. People drawn to cults very often come from families in crisis, and are consequently emotionally vulnerable. Cults very easily form surrogate families for these unfortunate individuals, "families with benefits," if you will.

Even more astounding to the student of belief is that this grip on the minds of disciples remains vigorously active long after the guru has died. Religious subjugation is a heinous form of slavery, given that it creates pawns that will defend their slavery and insist that they prefer it to other, less restrictive ways of living. I have spoken to cult members who can readily recognise the bondage of members of other cults, but are quite incapable of recognising or admitting their own.

That there is untruth in every orthodox version of events is a virtual certainty, as we have come to see thus far. But instead of exposing those elements of deception for what they are and leaving the skeleton of veracity for our further inspection, conspiracy theorists attempt to replace the whole model with one of even more insidiousness. They conjure up alternatives from the shadows of depravity for the most despicable of reasons: Conspiracy theorists are charlatans and scoundrels, and the damage they do to the quest for truth is incalculable.

It's an ill wind, however, that blows no good at all, and conspiracy theories provide the student of belief systems with rich turf for his studies. Not every belief is morally bad; and indeed, many are beneficial to society and leave people measurably better off while doing no substantial harm. On the other hand, conspiracy theories — if measured against their ability to bring us closer to truth and enlightenment — are a sociopathic blight.

The strange thing about belief is this — believing something makes one feel special. No matter what we believe in, we take an almost creepy delight in it. Perhaps that ineluctable, inordinately zealous, usually irrational defence of belief we so often find is a consequence of not wanting to lose the rewards it endows? Do we hear echoes of a smoker defending cigarettes, or the child frantically swaddling itself in a security blanket? Believing and instinct reward us in precisely the same ways. Taste makes eating a pleasure, and sexual thrills make the whole messy business of procreation a preferred destination; likewise, believing makes survival an exercise in gratification. Reality is not always palatable, but the sweetener of faith in a personal deity of whatever shape, size, or form certainly helps to make it rosy. That's why I stipulate that belief is an instinctual imperative. The writer Flannery O'Connor told us that truth does not change according to our ability to stomach it. I would add that truth does not improve by our propensity to believe a preferred version of it.

I'd like us to pause here for a moment and reflect. Here's the thing — belief doesn't wander around aimlessly, nor do we carriers of the germ all quietly retreat to mull over our beliefs in solitude for the rest of our days. Belief tends to organise itself, inside and out.

Cults provide the most focussed examples of organised belief — but there's a caveat. If we study cults to determine the truth about them generally, we need for the purposes of our initial study to ignore the one we might be part of ourselves. To achieve that, we should first and foremost learn with sufficient clarity just what a cult is, so that we can recognise the framework surrounding our thinking. As with gangs and tribes, I have defined cults somewhat more broadly than the standard view allows, conscious always not to depart from the spirit of the popular conception of these groups. I have done this in the interests of parsimony; rather than invent a new word, I have commandeered one from the lexicon, and adapted it to suit my purpose. I should hope the effectiveness of this approach will soon become apparent.

There is a thread that links gangs to mobs, cults, and sects, and even to the broader mass of religious groups. We can track the connection if we look first at gangs and work our way backwards to religion. Gangs are theatres of debauchery. They set up social islands wherein base urges are legitimate and encouraged as a sign of membership and rank within the group. In other words, they allow instincts to rule behaviour to the detriment of civilised constraint. A gang is an expression of protest and defiance that exaggerates the level of aggression required by instinct. Gangs and mobs seek the pleasurable rewards of instinct out of all proportion to their design. Sex, mating rituals, violence, turf warfare, territorial displays, and pack frenzy are all subverted to the worship of unconstrained hedonism.

Gang members live for the thrill of being an out-law. There are other bonding threads in gangs linked to survival in an inhospitable and forbidding social environ-ment, but the ultimate *raison d'être* of gangs, and equally of cults and sects, is to seek some modicum of purpose in life. It's a longing that can become quite desperate; and the greater the desperation, the more extreme the pack behav-iour becomes. In gangs, the pleasure-taking is general to the membership, whereas in cults and sects, members are subverted more to the dark pleasures of their leaders. Polyg-amy and sexual control are examples of how base instincts are expressed in cults. Of course, some cults exhibit group behaviour that is decent and beyond reproach, but they nevertheless commit themselves to satisfying the will and desires of their leadership. It's all just a question of scale, reflecting the degree to which packs of people throw off the constraints of social mores.

In the most general terms, a cult is a group of people who share a dogmatically held common purpose or belief. The word first appeared in the seventeenth century, and is derived from the Latin root *cultus* (meaning *to worship*). The term thus implied a religious grouping in its original form, making the description unexpectedly appropriate. There is a strong link between cults and worship, even in non-religious groups. The leaders of cults are invariably worshipped, and hero-worship reveals an oddly self-depre-cating human reaction to charisma. Sadly, this sort of blind adulation often has tragic consequences.

The concept of cults was embraced by sociology in the 1930s, and separated from the notion of sects, which differ in that they are born from ideological differences with a progenitor religious body. Sects form part of a lineage, creating continuity with mainstream ideas, whereas cults form quite spontaneously around the novel and unprecedented revelations of a particular individual. The primary difference between my definition of cults and the more usual one lies in the size or scope of the cult. They are generally held to be relatively small, fringe groups of disaffected individuals, but I have found that the glue that gives cults their cohesion is surprisingly independent of their size.

There is something sinister about cults. Viewed from the outside, they just don't seem kosher. Much as I try to remain objective, I must admit to a level of prejudice. The label "cult" is usually a pejorative term, and I wish I could free myself from that preconception. But — and this is a big but — I do not apologise for having ethical standards. Cults have only themselves to blame for the negative light in which they are often viewed. This has less to do with internal rites or doctrine — it is far easier to abhor Satanists than it is to dislike the relatively decent principles that drive Jehovah's Witnesses, for example — than it has with the *modus operandi* employed by cults to psychologically imprison their flocks. I think this is where I hit the nerve, for it is here that we find we can include the cults operating in the world of science.

Sociologists Stark and Brainbridge have given us the currently accepted definition of a cult: "A deviant religious organization with novel beliefs and practices."[8] Contingent upon the arguments raised in this book, I drop the

---

8 Rodney Stark and William Brainbridge, A *Theory of Religion* (New Brunswick, NJ: Rutgers University Press, 1996), 124.

word "religious" and see where that takes us. I should imagine that this is quite acceptable, because making cults inherently religious immediately excludes secular cults, of which there are many. They include the Shining Path guerrilla group, the 9/11 Truth movement, the Manson Family, the Roswell UFO conspiracy theorists, the Y2K and Mayan doomsday cults, and the fans of James Dean, to name but a few.

Mary Ann Sieghart provides a useful precis of the qualities that admit a social group to the ranks of cultism: "*It indoctrinates its members; it forms a closed, totalitarian society; it has a self-appointed, messianic and charismatic leader; and it believes that the ends justify the means.*"[9]

However, the choice of words is easily taken to be demeaning, and that carries an onerous overhead when we interview members in the course of studying cults. Let's be frank; from a sociological point of view, cults are not a good thing, no matter how deliriously happy its members may appear to be from time to time. Cults are a manifestation of belief, and as such (if I am to be trusted), they do objective truth a grave disservice. The fact remains that the five characteristics listed by Sieghart really do apply to cults, and we must deal with the negativity that comes with the bundle.

I daresay that none of the points made by Sieghart would be readily accepted by even a single member of any cult that I can think of, but it is also true that they would vehemently disagree with scholars of the phenomenon that their grouping is indeed a cult. And that brings us to another

---

9 Mary Ann Sieghart, "The cult figure we could do without", *The Times*, October 26, 2001.

important property of this type of social group: It is in the nature of cults, as with belief generally, that we consider our own as exclusively beyond criticism. It is something that affects social scientists studying cults as much as it does the subjects they are examining. We need to be very strict about this, or we shall end up guilty of producing blatant propaganda for whatever team we happen to bat for. If I were, say, a Scientologist, my scholarly investigation of cults would be overtly biased if I included Scientology as a case study. Furthermore, I would surely not use the term cult to describe my own group, preferring instead to insist that it is a glowing exception. That Scientology is a cult, embodying all the negatives that characterise cults, would be perfectly obvious to all but believing Scientologists. As a scholar, I need first to study other cults to determine the principles, and then, finally, apply them to my own situation as an exercise in self-realisation that might usefully follow scientific investigation.

One of the identifying markers put forward by Dr Sieghart is that cults form closed, totalitarian societies. Not all do, but it certainly applies to the majority of cults, enough to make it a strong pointer. Let's see if it fits a scientific group. The operators of the Large Hadron Collider, famous for their alleged "discovery" of the fabled Higgs boson, fit the bill rather nicely. The group is both closed and totalitarian. No one outside of the elite, almost invisible band of particle physicists admitted to the inner sanctum has any say on what goes on there. They do their work in secret and speak in a language few can understand, surfacing only occasionally to make selective announcements about the outcome of their rites.

Completely self-regulating, they answer to no one but themselves.[10]

Yes, they fit our definition of a cult quite comfortably.

Doctrinal oligarchs have two strings to their bow: consensus and authority. They succeed in their nefarious plots by creating the perception that they are, or exclusively represent, a privileged authority. It doesn't matter whether the authority being served may itself be at some considerable remoteness and probably unavailable for any sort of material personal interaction with most of us — for example, God, NASA, aliens — there is no shortage of self-appointed agents out there to bring us the good news. We are made to cower, almost literally, before these dominant authorities, as much in awe of their elevation in the hierarchy as we are fearful of their wrath. Then, in a *coup de grâce*, the whole thing is wrapped in a blanket of consensus and fraternal bonding, and voila! A cult is born.

There are several things we need to add to our understanding of cults, and they correlate neatly with what we shall soon reveal in our discussion of conspiracy theories. Firstly, we shall see (to our astonishment, no doubt) that this sort of behaviour is by no means limited to religionists. The halls of science are replete with cults, flying flags of every colour in the rainbow. Secondly, consensus is an internal term; it does not imply the aligned views of a majority in society, as it might in national politics, but instead describes consensus within the cult itself. Thirdly,

---

10 Eminent physicist Dr Alexander Unzicker blew the whistle on the Large Hadron Collider cult in his highly recommended book The Higgs Fake: How Particle Physicists Fooled the Nobel Committee (CreateSpace, 2013)

cults are gangs, just with moral arrogance thrown into the mix. This sense of moral high ground felt by the protagonists of a particular model draws them quickly into the club, and before long they too are fighting for it. It certainly explains why cult members tend to ignore or denigrate criticism.

Thus, we get a ruling class of physicists who call upon the irrefutable authority of Albert Einstein, and who jointly defend that position from the security of internal consensus. We get passionate Christians who invoke the infallible authority of the Pope as the sole agent of God on Earth, and who stand shoulder-to-shoulder against dissent. The 2012 doomsday cult believed without question in the authority of the Mayans as they saw it expressed in the notorious long-cycle calendar. There are many more examples: groups like Scientologists, Mormons, and al-Qaeda — that is to say, fanatical followers of L. Ron Hubbard, Joseph Smith, and Osama bin Laden respectively — as well as the flocks of Jim Jones, Charles Manson, David Koresh, Shoko Asahara, and Marshall Applewhite. In general, cult members seem to prostrate and abandon their common sense and rational minds before the outrageous and unverifiable claims of figures of authority.

Cults certainly provide very neat models of structured belief and illustrate quite usefully the behavioural nuances spawned by convictions. But for an even more eye-watering view of the unbridled licentiousness with which belief rewards its soldiers, we need look no further than conspiracy theories. Are they any more absurd than common or garden-variety religious sects? No, I don't think they are. What makes conspiracy theories especially negative to

objective science — they are unsurpassed in this regard —
is that they claim to a large extent to be based on science.
That is what makes them so distasteful to rational people
generally, and to scientists in particular.

Before I set out on the journey that would bring this
book to fruition, I had been seriously peeved by conspiracy misinformation (I'm being polite) that affected me
and my colleagues in space science directly, principally
the moon landing and chemtrail cults. The HAARP iono-
spheric research programme is sponsored mutually by the
US military and the University of Alaska. It's just the thing
that conspiracy theorists love to feast on, and they went
nuts over it. It has all the elements — space-age technology,
covert military involvement, Star Wars force fields; it's a
real Spy vs Spy omnibus.

The theories they came up with are, to anyone in the
know, absolute nonsense (and, to be honest, extremely
offensive), but that doesn't mean a row of beans to these
fellows. I have met some of them, and they matched their
sociological profiles perfectly. There is a strong environmental component to the HAARP conspiracy, and it wasn't
long before I realised that many of these groups are quite
incestuous. Close cousins in their war against civilisation
are the erstwhile chemtrail gang. I tried hard to reconnect
them with the truth of the matter, but it was hopeless. Their
typical response was that I must be part of the conspiracy.

Religions follow upon the conversion of theological
models into political movements, with all that the term
"political" implies. Concern for their own immortality is
something that seems to affect politicians and religionists
in equal measure. Both employ precisely the same method

to ensure that their doctrine flourishes in the minds of generations to come. Without exception, religious methodology relies upon indoctrination; it's their most important activity. For that reason, global groups like the Roman Catholic Church and Jehova's Witnesses are by my definition cults. They simply could not continue to exist without indoctrination.

Let's review. Mary Ann Sieghart lists the defining qualities of cults as follows:

- It indoctrinates its members;
- It forms a closed, totalitarian society;
- It has a self-appointed, messianic, and charismatic leader;
- It believes that the ends justify the means.

For the purposes of this book, I have been liberal with my definition of cults, in order to apply the above principles more broadly. The essential parameters defining a cult can be used to illuminate the workings of more nebulous groupings, provided they meet some or all of the points on Dr Sieghart's list. In my view, a great deal of overlap exists between cults and conspiracy theories.

Conspiracy theories trade upon the fundamental premise that there is an elaborate and painstaking official cover-up, and perhaps inadvertently expose the Achilles' heel of the scientific method. Belief skews our priorities and hog-ties our objective scepticism. The conspiracy theorist can say just about anything, no matter how outlandish, and it will be swallowed hook, line, and sinker — all it needs to do is make government look sufficiently sinister.

The intense scrutiny being torqued onto the official version of events is *entirely* absent from self-examination by protagonists of a conspiracy theory. Conspiracists make absolutely no attempt to falsify their conspiratorial hypothesis, in the scientific tradition. That alone makes their efforts non-science. Evidence rebutting the conspiracy idea doesn't get checked out. Not even a little bit. Conspiracy theorists are notoriously blinkered by their dogma, and admit no errors. Michael Shermer poses the essential question:

> Why do people believe in highly improbable conspiracies? I contend that it is because their pattern-detection filters are wide open, thereby letting in any and all patterns as real, with little or no screening of potential false patterns. Conspiracy theorists connect the dots of random events into meaningful patterns, and then infuse those patterns with intentional agency. Add to those propensities the *confirmation bias* and the *hindsight bias* (in which we tailor after-the-fact explanations to what we already know happened), and we have the foundation for conspiratorial cognition.[11]

Conspiracy theories go wrong where religions go wrong — instead of confining their scepticism to criticism of a particular version of events, they take the next step. They concoct a replacement theory, in great and comprehensive detail, as if they have some exclusive connection

---

11 Michael Shermer, *The Believing Brain* (New York: Times Books, 2011).

to the hidden truth. So consumed are they by their own grand beliefs that they paint a picture in vivid colours and fine resolution, as if that confirms their intimate relationship with some higher power. There is a clear analogy with religion.

Belief overwhelms our faculties for reason and intelligent discrimination, and nowhere is this more evident than in the 9/11 conspiracy theory. I chose that particular conspiracy group from a list of hundreds because it serves so well as an example of internally legitimised craziness. The collective face of alternative theories about the destruction of the World Trade Centre and the events that surrounded it on 11th September 2001 has an interesting name. It's called the Truth movement. What brilliant irony.

We don't have time to explore in depth the social backdrop to the notion that a privileged elite, or several such oligarchies, control many aspects of our daily lives by means of incredibly secretive conspiracies. For serious students of conspiracy theories, such background is essential, and I would urge those individuals to read at least two of my references on the subject, namely Michael Shermer's much-quoted *The Believing Brain* and Arthur Goldwag's *Cults, Conspiracies, & Secret Societies*[12]. Both provide excellent insight to the phenomenon by meticulous and even-handed scholars, and go into detail beyond the reach of this work.

For our purposes here, all we need concern ourselves with is that the emergence of an entrepreneurial class

---

12 Arthur Goldwag, *Cults, Conspiracies, & Secret Societies* (New York: Vintage Books, 2009).

after the nineteenth century industrial revolution created an elite social stratum of powerful capitalists whose battlefield is the global marketplace. These business leaders are essentially independent individuals with no discernible inclination to share the spoils with their competition, and by their nature they tend to avoid any form of leadership by committee. While some industrial and commercial corporations are immensely influential, the idea of a truly global conspiracy is far-fetched and without testable support.

So hungry are latent conspiracists for a conspiratorial cause in which to immerse themselves, that they will take up the cudgel for almost anything. What they promote seems to depend largely on how well presented the propaganda is, in other words, on the skill of spin doctors. Some conspiracy theories are so bizarre that no one even bothers trying to debunk them. Taking the cake is British journalist David Icke, who has built up a sizeable following of devoted fans and a full schedule of lucrative international speaking engagements based upon a fantastic conspiracy he has allegedly exposed.

You see, David Icke tells us with a straight face that he believes that humanity is being governed by alien reptiles with shapeshifting abilities. Yes, you did read that correctly. Our government officials are not human at all; in reality, they are form-changing alien lizards. It all started when Christine Fitzgerald, a former close friend of Princess Diana, alleged that the princess once told her that the British royal family were actually well-disguised reptiles from a distant galaxy. Icke's subsequent investigations uncovered even more horrifying facts: This alien control conspiracy goes far beyond the British royals. Arthur

Goldwag describes this cult in his book *Cults, Conspiracies, & Secret Societies*:

> When seeking to understand the conspiratorial mind,
> the focus of its obsession is less important than the
> obsession itself. Jim Marrs has published a string of
> best-sellers on everything from the Kennedy assassi-
> nations and the role played by space aliens in Biblical
> history to the complicity of US intelligence agencies
> in the events of 9/11. David Icke, a retired British soc-
> cer player and sports announcer turned writer and
> lecturer, has discerned a conspiracy of shape-shift-
> ing reptiles of extraterrestrial origin — among them
> the British royal family, the Bushes, Gorbachev, and
> Henry Kissinger — who are striving to subjugate the
> human race.[13]

The conspiracy theorists of more recent times have
tended to be more focussed in their conjecture, preferring
to pick on governments and their agencies as the manifestations of Big Brother. There is indeed some merit in
this point of view, and governments have only themselves
to blame. As more and more whistleblowers expose covert
activities, it lead one to wonder just how much secret
manipulation is actually going on. It is without doubt
more than we know. This pool of suspicion has become
the breeding place of wildly imaginative exaggerations
of the status quo, and leads directly to the formulation of

---

13 Ibid.

conspiracy theories. Almost any publicised event, from roadside bombs to the cutest wisps of fluffy white cloud, is tailed before long by those who claim to have uncovered the real story. To these individuals, everything, no matter how superficially innocent, is at its heart sinister, a dolled-up campaign by a diabolical government. Acts of terrorism are custom made for these folk, grist to their ravenous mill.

As we have seen time and again, belief is an immodest precursor to the contriving of supporting evidence. Zealous conspiracists see conspiracy where more sober analysts find the very suggestion ludicrous. Nowhere in the nearly fifty conspiracy theories that I examined for the purposes of this book is this propensity more obvious than with the 9/11 Truth movement. I'll leave it to the psychologists to figure out the mindset that spawns that sort of thing.

The terror attacks of 11 September 2001 were manna from heaven for the conspiracists idling in the wings for a fresh cause to subvert. Based on journalistic investigation, eyewitness reports, and photographic evidence, the events of the day appeared to roll out like this: After careful, detailed planning lasting years, al-Qaeda launched the most comprehensive and devastating terror attack in history on the morning of Tuesday, 11 September 2001. Nineteen al-Qaeda operatives hijacked four heavily fuelled long-haul airliners, took control of the flight decks, and diverted the aircraft towards four selected targets: one for the Pentagon (HQ of the US Defence Department), one aircraft each for the Twin Towers of the World Trade Center (WTC) in New York City, and the fourth for Washington DC. The last failed to reach its intended target following heroic intervention by the passengers.

The effects were catastrophic. There was serious structural damage to the Pentagon, resulting in a partial collapse on the western side, but it was the spectacular assault on the World Trade Center that remains forever fixed in memory. Captured on video, the impacts and subsequent fireballs were horrifying, and the damage so extensive, that al-Qaeda commanders later admitted that it far exceeded their expectations. So much so, they saw the hand of Allah itself fanning the flames. Within two hours, both towers had collapsed, taking all the buildings of the WTC complex down with them. A storm of debris and fire caused significant damage to ten other large buildings in the proximity. All in all, nearly three thousand people perished in the attack, including 227 passengers and crew, and nineteen hijackers (all positively identified) in the four jetliners. In 2004, Osama bin Laden claimed responsibility for the attacks. Subsequent investigation has revealed comprehensive details of the planning and commissioning of the entire operation from beginning to end.

One of the most incredible aspects of the conspiracy theory phenomenon is how quickly those who embrace these theories will bring themselves to bear upon an event. There is no doubt that the Internet assists them enormously in their endeavours, and in the case of 9/11, it was particularly effective.

I'd be interested to discover just why it was that some individuals felt the need to conjure up a conspiracy theory in the case of the 9/11 catastrophe. The pivotal argument raised by conspiracy theories is that officials have intentionally falsified the record of events, and as a result the wrong people are being blamed. What was it about the official 9/11 story that raised the conspiracists' eyebrows at the outset? Why was my own suspicion not piqued when I heard about the attack? The answers to these questions are telling.

We were told that al-Qaeda was responsible for those overt acts of terror on September 11th. What is it that might encourage one to take the view that al-Qaeda was an unlikely perpetrator? I can't think of anything that would trigger the suspicion that they were not to blame. I find it extremely plausible, without any further investigation, that a well-funded, well-organised, ideologically extreme international terror organisation like al-Qaeda, which had made explicit threats against the United States, and which had a robust track record in terrorism, would commission the operation. They had both the motive and the means. I certainly wouldn't rule them out *a priori*.

On the other hand, is it reasonable to suggest that the US government itself is a more likely perpetrator, or — in alternative versions of the conspiracy — the state of Israel? On balance of probability, one would have to lean strongly towards al-Qaeda. But for some reason not quite clear to the rest of us, the conspiracists chose from the beginning to remove al-Qaeda from the suspect list. Ignoring the most obvious perpetrators from the outset demonstrates the stupefying effect of a pre-existing mindset. The latent conspiracy theorist *wants* a conspiracy. All the "evidence" supporting conspiracy is therefore obtained by reverse engineering from a pre-ordained conclusion.

The March 2005 edition of *Popular Mechanics* carried a well-reasoned and intensively researched rebuttal of sixteen of the most vehement claims of the Truth movement. They introduce their analysis as follows:

Healthy skepticism, it seems, has curdled into para-
noia. Wild conspiracy tales are peddled daily on the
Internet, talk radio and in other media. Blurry photos,
quotes taken out of context and sketchy eyewitness
accounts have inspired a slew of elaborate theories:
The Pentagon was struck by a missile; the World
Trade Center was razed by demolition-style bombs;
Flight 93 was shot down by a mysterious white jet.
As outlandish as these claims may sound, they are
increasingly accepted abroad and among extremists
here in the United States.

To investigate 16 of the most prevalent claims made
by conspiracy theorists, *Popular Mechanics* assem-
bled a team of nine researchers and reporters who,
together with PM editors, consulted more than 70
professionals in fields that form the core content of
this magazine, including aviation, engineering and
the military.

In the end, we were able to debunk each of these
assertions with hard evidence and a healthy dose of
common sense. We learned that a few theories are
based on something as innocent as a reporting error
on that chaotic day. Others are the byproducts of cynical imaginations that aim to inject suspicion and
animosity into public debate. Only by confronting
such poisonous claims with irrefutable facts can we
understand what really happened on a day that is forever seared into world history.[14]

---

14 "Debunking the 9/11 Myths: Special Report", *Popular Mechanics*,
March 2005.

The Truth movement follows the well-worn evolution-ary path of gangs, and with time it too has become divided in power struggles and ideological fragmentation. We can nonethless still find some fairly representative articles of conspiracy that have been put forward by the movement as a whole. I shall present a handful of these examples for us to consider. The number of folks on this conspiracy bandwagon is rather daunting, and includes such superfi-cially impressive subsets as Architects & Engineers for 9/11 Truth, Pilots for 9/11 Truth, Scholars for 9/11 Truth, and so on, *ad nauseum*. I wouldn't be at all surprised if in one of my Internet searches I were to find a group going under the banner "Terrorists for 9/11 Truth." These attempts to attract public sympathy by projecting an aura of "expert testimony" surrounding the conspiracy idea are patently brittle how-ever, as further investigation quickly shows.

In the interests of brevity, I have chosen one conspiracy site to exemplify the Truth movement generally. It is called *911Truth.org*, and was selected purely because it was top of the list in my Google search for "9/11 truth". It seems fairly representative of the broader movement, and contains a schedule of their points of departure from the orthodox ver-sion of events (quoted verbatim):

- the unprecedented failure of the US air defense system on the morning of the attacks;
- the evidence that Flight 93 was shot down;
- contradictions and dubious evidence in the official claims about the alleged hijackers

and masterminds, and doubts about their real identities;

- signs that the alleged hijackers enjoyed high-level protection against discovery by honest investigators;
- evidence that the alleged hijackers were financed by states allied with US intelligence;
- widespread signs of official foreknowledge and, in fact, advance preparation for the 9/11 attack scenario;
- the long-running links between Islamist fundamentalist terror cells and US covert operations, dating back to CIA support for the anti-Soviet mujahedeen and Osama Bin Ladin [sic] himself;
- the demolition-like collapse of the Twin Towers and of a third skyscraper, WTC 7;
- and questions concerning who could have logically expected to derive benefit in the aftermath of a massive attack on the United States.

There are many more strings to the conspiracists' bow than just these; I show the list simply to illustrate conspiratorial thinking. If one is to evaluate initiatives like *911Truth.org*, one must of course look at the counterarguments and explanations coming from the opposing camp. There are several, but I would suggest *debunking911.com*. It seems to me the most cohesive and comprehensive rebuttal site for the 9/11 conspiracies. Reference is also made to the official, peer-reviewed National Institute of Standards and Technology (NIST) report on the entire 9/11 incident. Of crucial specific interest is the NIST Engineering Laboratory's *Questions and Answers about the NIST WTC Towers Investigation web page,* which offers a concise and incisive list of thirty-four popular questions being posed by those inferring government collusion and conspiracy in the 9/11 attacks.[15] It concerns itself only with those questions relating to the structural engineering aspects of the catastrophe. If any single document is cited as reference for the conventional view, it should be this one in my opinion.

The NIST Q&A report answers *inter alia* the following crucial questions, which should clear up most of the scepticism regarding the destruction of the World Trade Center:

- What caused the collapses of WTC 1 and WTC 2?
- Why didn't NIST consider a "controlled demolition" hypothesis with matching computer modelling and explanation like it did for the "pancake theory" hypothesis?
- Weren't the puffs of smoke that were seen, as the collapse of each WTC tower starts, evidence of controlled demolition explosions?
- How could the WTC towers collapse in only 11 seconds (WTC 1) and 9 seconds (WTC 2) — speeds that approximate that of a ball

---

15 Link to the NIST Q&A report:
nist.gov/el/disasterstudies/wtc/faqs_wtctowers.cfm

dropped from similar height in a vacuum (with no air resistance)?

- Since the melting point of steel is about 1,500 degrees Celsius (2,800 degrees Fahrenheit) and the temperature of a jet fuel fire does not exceed 1,000 degrees Celsius (1,800 degrees Fahrenheit), how could fires have impacted the steel enough to bring down the WTC towers?
- Did the NIST investigation look for evidence of the WTC towers being brought down by controlled demolition? Was the steel tested for explosives or thermite residues?

MY AIM HERE is not to list every question and give the answers contained in the report; that would take a chapter on its own. I would hope that those sincerely seeking the truth of the matter will use the provided links to investigate the issue for themselves. I wish merely to illustrate that every single one of the assertions of the 9/11 Truth movement has been cogently rebutted by independent professionals, using the highest standards of physical science. Most of the material in the literature is naturally centred on the WTC, because that was the most catastrophic point of attack. There is in addition equally compelling evidence showing that the damage to the Pentagon was indeed caused by American Airlines flight 77; that the US Air Force response was as expected under the circumstances; that the crash site of United Airlines flight 93 was consistent with the scenario deduced from the Black Box, the Cockpit Flight Recorder, and civilian cellphone conversations with passengers, and showed no evidence of having been shot down; and that the assertions concerning the supposed intentional demolition of WTC building 7 are baseless, contrived, and without any credible physical evidence.

What strikes me is that the Truth movement has not rescinded a single claim in the face of counter evidence. The assertion seems to be that every single one of their points about 9/11 is beyond reasonable doubt, thus above the reach of rational criticism. That smacks strongly of undiluted belief and the defence of convictions, and militates against the notion that their hypotheses are based upon science and objective data. That they claim to be perfectly right in all respects should in itself give the lie to their appeal to scientific reason.

It is interesting also to note that up to the time of this book's publication, some thirteen years after the event, not a single person has owned up to taking part in the cover-up conspiracy. Nor has any perpetrator been found by forensic investigation and brought before the courts. The extent of the required effort, and the sheer numbers of people and organisations that would have had to be involved, are the strongest indicator that the 9/11 Truth movement is in fact the 9/11 Untruth movement.

Clearly, to say that conspiracy theories are unconvincing is a towering understatement; one has to be possessed by an obsessive predilection for sinister plots (and probably an overripe contempt for authority) to entertain the wild reasoning of conspiracists. Conspiracy theories depend critically on one thing: a complete absence of any objective test of any of the contentious points they raise. I have many times encountered this first-hand. Along with my friends at NASA, I tried with great patience to explain to Apollo landing deniers that every anomaly they imagine can be quite easily put to rest with just a basic grasp of the science involved. Most often, all that a reasonable doubter needs is an elementary physics lesson to illuminate the holes in his pet theories. Unfortunately, reasonably objective conspiracists seem not to exist on planet Earth. In my experience, they just glaze over when you're trying to explain how the mission was actually achieved.

And yet, conspiracies of the kind they describe are unlikely to work in reality for precisely the same reason they were concocted in the first place — human nature. Human beings cannot keep a secret. If there ever were such a conspiracy, sooner or later at least one of the conspirators would blab — be it for ten minutes of fame, revenge, money, pressure, or simply a desire for salacious scandal. Michael Shermer tells of Gordon Liddy's experience:

> But as G. Gordon Liddy once told me, the problem with government conspiracies is that bureaucrats are incompetent and people can't keep their mouths shut. Liddy should know as he was an aide to President Nixon and one of the masterminds behind the break-in of the Democratic National Committee offices at the Watergate Hotel. Complex conspiracies are difficult to pull off — in this case even something as simple as a hotel burglary was foiled by a security guard, and under pressure of congressional hearings and journalistic investigations many of the conspira-

cists cracked and talked. So many people want their quarter hour of fame that even the men in black couldn't squelch the squealers from spilling the beans. Once again, there's a good chance that the more elaborate a conspiracy is, and the more people that would need to be involved to pull it off, the less likely it is true.[16]

No one denies that people in powerful positions behave rather strangely most of the time. They seem to be too secretive for their own good, and they invite suspicion by their lack of transparency. But to automatically read conspiracy into their shyness with the truth is an overreaction. Sometimes, puzzling behaviour on the part of those in command of influential processes is driven by political savvy rather than by some sinister, covert drive for global domination.

Secrets are more often than not kept to simply protect the favoured ideology, but it must be said that the whole business of covert behaviour is overdone, as we've seen time and again with the "-gates" — just ask Nixon about Watergate and Phil Jones about climategate. Keeping secrets from the paying public is a dangerous game. But there is a world of difference between a hidden political agenda and conspiracy. Not all attempts at aligning with a favoured political position are sinister. Very often it's no more than a desire to appear politically correct. The Nobel Prize is a case in point. Once a grand award for excellence

---

16 Michael Shermer, *The Believing Brain* (New York: Times Books, 2011).

in scientific research, the Nobel Prize has regressed to an iconic symbol now favouring scientists who play the political game for reward, instead of the hardy few pursuing the unadorned truth. The list of physics laureates tells the story.

The rewarding of closed-loop, model-aligned empirical results in the scientific field has become blatant over time, culminating with the 2013 physics prize going to François Englert and Peter Higgs *"for the theoretical discovery of a mechanism that contributes to our understanding of the origin of mass of subatomic particles, and which recently was confirmed through the discovery of the predicted fundamental particle, by the ATLAS and CMS experiments at CERN's Large Hadron Collider."* In 1978, Penzias and Wilson were rewarded for discovering the cosmic microwave background radiation (CMBR); in 2006, Mather and Smoot received the prize for revealing the blackbody nature and anisotropy in the CMBR; and in 2011, Riess, Perlmutter, and Schmidt were recognised for discovering in supernova data that universal expansion is speeding up. None of these conclusions could have been reached without selectively filtering the data through the standard models. Analysis absent a preconceived theoretical paradigm would have produced results starkly at odds with those that received the Nobel accolade.

In science, the process of canonisation is relatively easy to see, and we begin to get a glimmer of understanding of why we cannot resist falling in love with theoretical models. Ideally, the process should be:

- observation → measured data →
  conjecture →

- hypothesis → prediction → multiple independent tests →
- confirmation or falsification → hypothesis becomes theory or is abandoned →
- theory is tested → theory becomes law or is abandoned →
- laws are used to build models.

In practice, however, the process these days is far from that ideal. The pure form of the scientific method starts with observation or experience of something in nature that requires elucidation. What we have nowadays is conjecture (mathematical brainstorming) leading to hypotheses, which are built into a hypo-stack containing multiple tuneable parameters, which leads in turn to adjustable predictions, and the eventual creation of a fail-proof model of some or other aspect of existence. This type of model has a built-in, dogmatic defence against falsification. If the preferred conclusion to the logical processes within the model's formalism is glorious enough, or awesome enough, then the model is inevitably canonised, no matter what anomalies it throws up.

A couple of years ago my friend and advisor Professor Paul Jackson emailed me from his redoubt Voëlvlei, in the lee of South Africa's Karkloof mountains. He attached an article from the September issue of *American Scientist* written by University of Cardiff astronomer Dr Mike Disney. It is entitled, *"Modern Cosmology: Science or Folktale?"* It struck a chord with me; resonated with ideas that were tumbling about in my mind. I met Dr Disney at the first Crisis in Cosmology Conference in 2005, where he presented a paper comparing the free parameters (aka tuning knobs) of Big Bang theory with actual measurements. Mike Disney showed that with this type of modelling, one can adjust parameters without shame to achieve a perfect match between hypothesis and observation. The correlation between model and harsh reality becomes more tenuous with each twiddle, but that matters not a whit. The glory of the idea triumphs over practical considerations, and the disingenuous perpetrators of these things are smothered in Nobel Prizes. Cosmology is a barely disguised fairy tale.

We will not successfully bring the matter of cosmology to a useable conclusion unless we first rid the whole affair of an effect I have named investment bias[17]. Nobel Laureate Robert Laughlin tells amusingly in his book *A Different Universe*[18] of the "First Theorem of Science", attributed to his colleague George Chapline: *"It is impossible to convince a person of any true thing that will cost him money"*.

No, it is not a sinister, political conspiracy; it is simply economics, and the currency is the dollar, plus, more significantly, exposure of individuals to the diabolical possibility that after so much effort, they might just have been wrong.

---

17 Investment bias: the subjective prejudice applied to scientific endeavour in order to align results with the outcome mooted in motivation for funding, and thereafter the pressures felt by scientists to maintain that position — is an extraordinarily powerful influence on scientific results, and needs to be clearly defined, recognised, and incorporated both into the literature and into data analysis, along with whichever other biases might skew the results.

18 Robert B. Laughlin, *A Different Universe (Reinventing Physics from the Bottom Down)* (Cambridge, MA: Basic Books, 2005).

In the wake of the nineteenth-century industrial revolution in Britain, technology boomed and science became a new god. The laws of thermodynamics — including the notion of entropy — came directly from the invention of steam engines (and not the other way around). For the first time in recorded history, engineers led social revolution. At the same time, astronomy flourished at dazzling speed. The technical excellence of optical instruments advanced in leaps and bounds, driven not by greed or territorial ambition, but by our innate exploratory drive. Our awe increased, and with it, our reverence for the new elders of the faith — scientists that pushed the frontiers of knowledge by dragging them ever outwards with an engine called imagination. Humankind's adulation was reaching the threshold of fan hysteria.

The great danger in theoretical modelling lies in the seductiveness of having one's personal opinions raised to the level of universal relevance. Before long, theorists start to believe that what they imagine is actually real, and that the novel products of their conjecture may legitimately be termed "discoveries". In more arcane realms of science, this sort of delusion is rampant, and syncopated thoughts are called discoveries without embarrassment or shame. A recent announcement by the science forum *Phys.org*[19] is a pertinent example of what we talking about. The press release was greeted with enthusiasm in world of theoretical astronomy. Cosmologists were happy. Here is an excerpt:

---

19 *phys.org/news/2013-11-nuclear-cooling-neutron-stars-deepens.html*

Writing in the journal *Nature*, Hendrik Schatz and colleagues describe a newly discovered process that happens within the star's crust, located just below the surface. Until now, scientists thought that nuclear reactions within the crust contributed to the heating of the star's surface.

"We previously thought that these reactions were strong enough to heat up the crust," said Schatz, an MSU professor of physics and astronomy. "But that's not the case."

What the team of scientists found is that in the star's crust near the surface there is a layer where nuclear reactions cause rapid neutrino cooling. Neutrinos are very elementary particles that are created through radioactive decay and pass very quickly through matter.

Reading the quoted passage, I am given the strong impression that these gentlemen have actually discovered something in the crust of a neutron star. They are talking as if they have studied an event on an actual neutron star, and that it increases our understanding of these mysteriously fascinating cosmological objects. As an astrophysicist intensely interested in neutron stars and with privileged access to the literature surrounding them, I know that the assertion being put forward by the authors of the quoted study is patently false, and it tweaks the word discovery in a terribly misleading way.

It is crucially important to emphasise that the "discovery" of nuclear cooling in a neutron star is not an empirical event, but merely a nuance of the developing model, seen nowhere but on a computer screen. I think the issue is that the discovery was not made on a neutron star. No discoveries have ever been made on a neutron star. Apart from an ambiguous spectral signature assigned to them by the developers of the model, they have never been observed, much less studied in detail. It is just a model, with arbitrarily tuneable parameters. That's fine, but they should make it clear in their announcement.

I would suggest that theorists would serve us better if they referred to observational data in developing models of hypothesised entities. The Sun is potentially a candidate progenitor of a neutron star, and what happens on the Sun can guide us in trying to imagine what would remain after the end game of a normal star.

Evidence of faith is yet more faith. I cannot say with certainty that black holes do not exist, any more than I could legitimately assert without any doubt whatsoever that God does not exist. Both would be physically impossible in terms of my grasp of physics, but then again, I'm still engaged in a lifelong struggle to properly explain what I see and experience directly, stuff that I can in principle measure and put under my microscope. I see no useful purpose in incorporating into my understanding those flimsy ghosts of human superstition.

My rule of thumb is that patently irrational things are excluded from the body of knowledge I carry with me; my library of opinions should reflect those things that I am reasonably certain of, and which I can confidently build into my understanding of the cosmos. I become certain not from the degree of comfort that I derive from my beliefs, but from rational, testable evidence emanating from objective enquiry. Clearly, the evidence I am speaking of should not have come from filtering experimental or observational data through the sieve of a preferred model.

Make no mistake; this will be no easy task. The requirement of objectivity may well be one of the most difficult things one could ever expect of our eternally hapless human creature. But if we do not try, we are condemned by our desire for comfort to remain unto death imprisoned in the quicksand of our beliefs.

My friend Harry Rose made a comment on Facebook about the function of Planck's constant h that I feel puts the erring of science into clear focus:

> And this immaterial nonsense … is the basis of Quantum physics … it's pseudo science (magical thinking, to be precise) and has become a religion (a philosophy accepted as truth). What you need to understand is this: in physics matter serves as the agent of objectivity … remove it and there is nothing by which theories of physics can be falsified, the consequences of which we can see high and wide. Physics has become a zoo of concepts that can't be verified. The physics of 'h' is a road to nirvana, spiritually pleasing, but unscientific.

I suppose, in the cold light of day, we'll eventually come to realise that black holes (and dark matter, dark energy), like conspiracy theories and indeed religion, are just shadows in the minds of people inclined to think like that.

Congratulations. We have now come face-to-face with those foxy things that all this hullaballoo is about: Belief and instinct. As we shall see in the next chapter, they are irrevocably bound together in eternal conflict. It is that fiery battle that creates and hones our personalities, so I guess we ought to get a handle on it if we want to get anywhere.

The road to hell isn't paved with gold, it's paved with faith.

JAROD KINTZ, THIS BOOK IS NOT FOR SALE

Mein Leyden O Herz Jesu Christ, meins Herzens beste Labsahl ist

Belief is a powerful agency. Belief shapes our thinking and guides our behaviour to such an extent that we often become blind to the chicanery of snake oil charlatans. We sometimes let our adulation turn us into factories blithely manufacturing imaginary evidence to support premises founded upon nothing more than slick illusion.

7

THE MYSTERY OF
PROPERTY AND NATIONS

What we're really fighting about

"IMAGINE THERE'S NO COUNTRIES, it isn't hard to do; nothing to kill or die for, no religion too ..." Thus sang the late John Lennon. It's hard to resist being seduced by such passionate idealism. At the same time, I recall the stark irony of how John Lennon died — at the hands of a raging Mad Hatter with a belief and a gun, and with as much dignity as a winter-cold New York City paving stone could provide. The lyrics of Elton John and Bernie Taupin's tearful requiem *"Empty Garden"* ring in my mind, and the spreading pool of my thoughts soon reaches out to embrace the assassination of Mahatma Gandhi too. Somehow, I must dig deep and find a way to express the profound lesson that lies interred with their bones. I come to bury Caesar, not to praise him.

In the 1960s, anthropologist-turned-playwright-turned-anthropologist Robert Ardrey published two books: first,

African Genesis in 1961, and then the landmark *The Territo-rial Imperative* in 1966. In the early 70s, my younger sister, then a liberal arts student at the University of Natal in Piet-ermaritzburg, gave me the latter book as a birthday gift, and for that I could never thank her enough. It gave me my first personal experience of a paradigm shift, and tonight, some forty years later, I have it open before me as I type. I have read ravenously since childhood, and have a personal library comprising several hundred important books. None is as important as this one. Nothing comes near, not even Newton's *Principia*. I'd like to quote the whole book, but we'll have to be satisfied with just a few paragraphs.

> A territory is an area of space, whether of water or earth or air, which an animal or group of animals defends as an exclusive preserve. The word is also used to describe the inward compulsion of animate beings to possess and defend such a space. A territo-rial species of animals, therefore, is one in which all males, and sometimes females too, bear an inherent drive to gain and defend an exclusive property.
>
> In most but not all territorial species, defence is directed only against fellow members of the kind. A squirrel does not regard a mouse as a trespass-er. In most but not all territorial species — not in chameleons, for example — the female is sexually unresponsive to an unpropertied male. As a general pattern of behaviour, in territorial species the com-petition between males which we formerly believed was one for the possession of females is in truth for the possession of property.

We may also say that in all territorial species, without exception, possession of a territory lends enhanced energy to the proprietor. Students of animal behaviour cannot agree as to why this should be, but the challenger is almost invariably defeated, the intruder expelled. In part, there seems some mysterious flow of energy and resolve which invests a proprietor on his home grounds. But likewise, so marked is the inhibition lying on the intruder, so evident his sense of trespass, we may be permitted to wonder if in all territorial species, there does not exist, more profound than simple learning, some universal recognition of territorial rights.[1]

My later contemplations of these things would show that in our particular species there is an alarming extension to the manic defence of territory. We take the same stance with ideas. *"Beware the man with a theory,"* my late father advised me, and how wise he was. Homo sapiens will bleed to stagnation rather than surrender its beliefs.

Statistically, wars between nations have decreased markedly since 1945. But conflict has not. Conflict has increased and spread to become history's first truly global conflagration. Wars are still with us, but it's deceiving; the nature of warfare has changed. Wars have transformed from combat *between* nations to fighting *within* nations. The tribal territory for which blood is endlessly spilt is virtual, ideological,

---

1 Robert Ardrey, *The Territorial Imperative: A Personal Inquiry into the Animal Origins of Property and Nations* (New York: Athenium, 1966).

and starkly independent of geographical boundaries. It's doctrine without borders.

The United States has lost its tribal soul. Let me rephrase that: The United States has never had a tribal soul. Nor has the Republic of South Africa. Long before they were organised into a union of states and republic respectively, these two countries were fluid collections of tribal territories, and in both cases, European settlers tried to weld those disparate souls into nationhood. In both cases, new regimes have replaced the old, and they promise that we shall eat cake. My fear, quite contrary to my wish, is that they will fail, in both cases.

There is an urgent and potentially life-saving lesson in this for us: Whatever we propose in our idealistic quest for utopia, it should not sail in the teeth of our design paradigm. We have cellular imperatives that will triumph in the end no matter what bright ideas we come up with. We might propose that the battle against HIV-AIDS can be won if we all become celibate. However, that's not going to happen. We may suggest that the solution to human misery lies in an end to war. Again, it's not going to happen. Some insist that utopia will follow the slaying of global religions. Sorry, that isn't going to happen either. We could even go so far as to say that we can conquer global hunger by abandoning greed. No, we aren't going to abandon greed, I'm afraid. Can we solve the road accident problem by banning alcohol? Not even that will work. The answer lies in undiluted pragmatism.

It seems to me that the social fabric of tribes across the globe is frayed and wearing thin. There appears to be some correlation with our growing detachment from reality. We have already discussed the effect of mathematics on our world view, but social decline is by no means limited to students of advanced calculus. The Internet, cellphones, television, and other forms of mass media have drastically changed the way we live and interact. Our species has adopted a cyber reality over the natural one, and it shows in awful ways. The dreadful cruelty, and loss of sensitivity to the value of life generally, reflects a downslide in moral values that increases the frequency and extent of sociopathic episodes in disparate societies.

The coldness and unreachable isolation of minds behind suicide-bomb terrorism, and the completely impersonal mass murders at schools, temples, and places of entertainment are frightening, hideous badges on the cloaks of modern man.

The difference — and this is critical — between these and historical acts of terror is that previously, they were the work of insular, lonely psychopaths who were considered genetic freaks. Nowadays we see terror being manifested in groups numbering from two or three to hundreds. Increasingly, we find groups of friends — usually youngsters — linked by some secret doctrine, going forth to make a statement in the blood of innocents. There has been a distinct shift in the last three decades from isolated, antisocial criminal acts to deliberate, violent social strategy. Sociopathic behaviour, and the mindset that feeds it, can be learnt in the superficial, virtual normality of the twenty-first-century milieu. This realisation sent a shiver up my spine.

I shall continue to use the United States and Republic of South Africa as examples upon which we can bounce our thoughts. They are not the sole proprietors of mankind's pathological behaviour, but they are well known enough to serve as useful models in our analysis. The United States became a proud melting pot for foreign settlers, who attempted to gel the parts by marginalising their slaves and, of course, the natives. Basically, they oppress non-whites. Today's South Africa is fondly referred to as the Rainbow Nation, a melee of tribes that tries hard to glue itself into common purpose by marginalising and oppressing non-blacks. The principle is the same; only the colour is different.

The dominant tribal quasi-souls in South Africa manifest not only in anti-whiteness, but in xenophobia as well. As I write, the TV screen rolls dramatic scenes of violent assault by native South Africans on Somali shopkeepers in one of the central provinces. It's a tribal soul talking, and talking loudly. Indians and those of mixed race are sidelined: mere garnishing on the political model. Both South Africa and the United States have liberal constitutions that were formulated by the loftiest imaginable human thought — so esteemed, in fact, that many claim that they were inspired by no less than divine providence itself. Yet, when the pack instinct kicks in, all the noble thoughts and faultless arguments in those superb declarations of human principle are about as effective as a lamb bleating in a thunderstorm.

Let's summarise the instinct-versus-ethics theme of the preceding paragraph: Mobs smells blood, and frenzy results. Ultimately, one tribe (or political party or race or religion, whatever) will rule, and opposing tribes will be sidelined. One gang will rule the turf, and the other plays the role of pretender. Both the United States and South Africa will demonstrate, in the fullness of time, that the instinct for tribal territory will overrule any noble political desire for egalitarianism. The rainbow wrapped around our perception of South Africa is an ephemeral dream coat, a lacy frill that casts its illusions only as long as the ground-swell territorial gangsterism allows it.

Man the individual and man the gangster will go to war over turf. Gangs are cults on steroids, driven by poverty and an absence of meaningful franchise to annexe their neighbourhood. The 'hood is everything: the castle of all they love and hold dear. So they unilaterally declare inde-pendence, set up their own distinct social structures, and paint their flags in graffiti, wherever you look. That's what I mean when I say gangsterism: the grassroots political expression of territory.

Those of us who stay well clear of street gangs invariably have the panacea of relative prosperity and comfortable middle-class privilege to keep us happy. Drugs tend to blur the boundaries between gangsters and non-gangsters, but it is nevertheless wealth and property that most often appease our wilful inclination to walk on the wild side. Gangsters are social misfits, and although that sometimes attracts peo-ple who are relatively well off — consider biker gangs, for example — it is most often poverty and social rejection that fuel the mob's blind fury. Wealth serves to insulate those of material privilege from the sordidness of life on the street. It is a primal polarity.

Recent events involving terrorism in Boston, and the var-ied reactions to them, have given me a vector along which I can move closer to the core of human instinct. The Arab Springs too have provided a tearful but profound lesson in sociology. The various uprisings have lost their noble veneer, exposing savagery at a level that tests scientific analysis to breaking point. As always, I try to reduce the system being studied to first principles, and let the rational waters flow whither they will. The first step in that process is to isolate the essential polarity. In human sociopolitical behaviour, the primary polarity emerging from the instinct-versus-free-will dichotomy is extreme conservative versus extreme liberal.

The superficial polarity of the Arab Spring syndrome was democracy versus dictatorship. The mobs went into the streets and demanded freedom. That's what mobs do, and they punctuate their demands with Molotov cocktails. Governments reacted severely and violently in a baptism of teargas and bullets. That's what threatened governments do. So all in all, it seemed to be just another day at the office. As events played out, however, the deeper dynamic emerged. Hidden power plays disguised themselves in the colours of both sides, and ultimately these third forces emerged as victors who claimed the spoils. The man in the street was left bombed and broken and hungry.

The term "sectarian violence" was born out of the conflicts in the Middle East. It is not limited to the Arab world by any means, but they have grown the phenomenon from faction fighting and family feuds to full-blown civil war. The territorial imperative and instincts driving human social units manifest themselves clearly in the Arab Springs, with the added value of even deeper fragmentation of people, norms, and values. The polarising subsets — in many cases no more than Sunni against Shi'a factionalism — provided the cannon fodder for ideologues in opposing camps. The ongoing holocaust in Syria paints a stark picture of a primary polarity morphing into multidimensional mob warfare, and the teeming refugee camps reveal with eye-watering clarity just what the silent majority thinks of it. We watch and learn.

The essence of nationalism is not dependent on scale. It can spread itself far more widely than the borders of a country, and indeed, exists also in smaller pockets within the political boundaries of nations. This tribal division can skew our view of nationalist campaigns. In the Norwegian summer of 2011, a formerly nondescript young man named Anders Breivik set off a bomb outside government buildings in Oslo, then travelled purposefully to Utøya island, where he used automatic weapons to gun down dozens of Norwegian children at a summer rally.

Breivik had developed the mindset of a terrorist, and that means he had lost respect for human life. Society through his eyes became dehumanised, the analogue of a cyber game, and the grassroots political landscape had morphed into a killing field where individuals were no longer real. He walked around killing children as if in a trance. It was the kind of trance commonly seen in players of *World of Warcraft*. That's something we ought to be thinking about very deeply.

The effect of mobs is independent of how well they represent truth. Mobs are always the minority, and they are always destructive. If gangs are cults on steroids, then activism is belief on steroids. It does not represent the will of the people. I had the pleasure the other day of watching the men's tennis final at the French Open. The unfolding drama between two masters of their craft, Rafa Nadal and Novak Djokovic, riveted a global television audience of millions, including me. At a critical point in the match, just as Rafa was about to make a vital serve, four activists brought the whole proceeding to a halt by protesting I care not what. In effect they were a mob, imposing their will upon the millions who had other priorities. Recently, over a cup of tea, incisive South African political analyst Denis Beckett said to me, "People get excited when they report that 10,000 people gathered to protest in a square in Egypt, but they totally ignore the eighty million Egyptians who stayed at home."

The great disappointment emerging from the roll-out of democracy is not how well it gives expression to the will of the people, but how badly that will aligns with the noble ideals of its liberal architects. We must acknowledge that democracy fairly practiced elects people, not ideas. Electioneering claptrap is neither convincing to the voter nor binding upon the claptrapper. We will time and again elect a particular person, and the motivation for choosing candidates in most cases has little to do with their ability to govern to any particular managerial or moral standards, and a whole lot to do with the colour of a flag. Americans will vote for a chap for no other reason than that he is either Republican or Democrat. Territorial tribalism trumps a master's degree in political science any day.

There is a gaping disparity between the theoretical will of people and the reality demonstrated by their tribal behaviour. Ants don't want to be free of an absolute queen. Lions are quite happy having alpha males. Humans want to be led. Anarchy will always fail as a social system because of that simple fact. The blaring trumpets of civil liberty may for a while drown out the quieter song of territorially secure anthropoids, but they are ultimately silenced by the irresistible tide of instinctive social behaviour. History bears sullen witness to the subjective brittleness of ideals when faced by the snarling adrenalin of a parent protecting its young.

Conflict between nations has nothing to do with the ideologies they represent. The United States did not square up to the USSR because it disliked communism; Israel does not threaten pre-emptive strikes against Iran in order to show disapproval of Islam; Tibet does not resent China as a consequence of China's internal political programme; the Vietnamese surely did not put themselves through the fires of hell because they found the Unites States's brand of democracy distasteful.

In all cases, the action from both sides is triggered by a threat to territory. One side makes the threat; the other reacts to it. It's all about turf. It's as true for the family unit as it is for nations. Instinctively, we're all gangsters.

I find the correlation between tribal culture (territorial imperative) and religion fascinating. Thus we have Sunni vs Shi'a in Islam, the Roman Catholic Church vs the rest, separation of Greek and Russian Orthodox, Chinese Buddhism pitted against Tibetan Buddhism, etc., etc. It seems to me that after the founder or figurehead of a religion dies, tribal and cultural influences begin to exert dominance over the original philosophy, and it splits along demographic and sociopolitical lines.

It's an instinct. We behave territorially because our instinct tells us to. The agreements and treaties and statements of intent that we so earnestly sign with one another have no more effect on our ultimate destiny than the rooster's habitual crowing has on the Sun.

Nationalism is an expression of the territorial urge. It affects our thinking and our judgement no less profoundly than any other instinct, and sometimes it pops up in surprising places. The controversial case of murdered British student Meredith Kercher, and the role played by American Amanda Knox in her demise, was brought back to the headlines by a retrial. Knox was first found guilty, then acquitted on appeal, and finally found guilty again by retrial in the Italian high court.

During her trial, and after her return to the United States, Amanda Knox received vigorous support from parties protesting her innocence. Web sites sprang up, and various individuals — from forensic investigators to crime authors to pastors — embarked on a pro-Knox campaign that was almost evangelical in its zeal. What was not surprising is that they were all American; the tribal connection was blatant.

There is no doubt in my mind that Homo sapiens is a territorial species, and that territory defines its behaviour. If we were to single out just one of the instinctive drives guiding us through life, it would have to be the subtle but hugely influential impetus that determines that we have property and nations.

Here we need to switch channels. People are social creatures. It's a wired-in imperative, no less influential in us than it is in ants, monkeys, weaver birds, sardines, bees, and elephants. Locked into our cells is a design template that constrains us as a species and is the central lynchpin that allows us to procreate and continue the mystifying relay race called life. The way that we arrange our lives, and the way that we think (though not specifically *what* we think) is predetermined and obstinately inflexible. We run on an operating system just as precisely coded as — and no less dictatorial than — Windows or Android; general policy governing Homo sapiens is predetermined from antiquity, and our free will tends to be obedient to it. Part of that overarching strategy is the pressing need to compartmentalise our seemingly random reactive thoughts into reinforcing rods we call *convictions*. Sloppy ideas just don't cut the mustard on planet Earth, so the management programme steps in and urges us to get a grip. As we develop opinions, so the instinctive regime shapes them and rewards them and gives them a compelling feel-good factor.

We represent a synthesis between two distinct pressures on the way we interact with the environment. The polarity at play in human behaviour is a dynamic represented at one extreme by instinct and at the other by belief; in between lies a narrow buffer called free will. Instinct is a code inherited at birth and belief is a reaction to environmental stimuli in real time.

The nineteenth-century British poet Samuel Butler left us this classic: A hen is only an egg's way of making another egg. The real, overriding intelligence resides in the egg, not the chicken, despite whatever freedom of choice the chicken thinks it has. We are no different. The dominant intelligence is in our atoms, not our minds. That cellular chemical intelligence is primordial, it would seem, and it determines *a priori* how we are to behave as a species.[2]

---

2 Biological, Darwin-type evolution describes a linear process of maturation of a species collectively, not of individuals per se. I am inclined to

The essential question, the one to which I am dragged kicking and screaming, is this: Could *intelligence* have been the product of evolution? From a state where there was no intelligence, could it have sprung forth? Think carefully about the notion of intelligence as a logical step in a chain of chemical reactions, ignoring for the time being a vexing lack of viable alternative theories. The corollary closely tied to this theorem is whether *life* could have evolved? From a crucible of sterile chemical ashes, is it conceivable or even remotely possible that a living thing could have arisen?

Human behaviour is driven or at least enhanced by the same set of psychochemical fight-or-flight secretions that flow in the blood of Vervet monkeys and Steppe wolves; whether we are contentedly accepting or angrily aggressive is underpinned by biochemistry, and it is those chemicals that to a large extent define our personalities. The same sort of subconscious stimulus that fires up our defence of nest and offspring does duty in our obsessive protection of the opinions stamping identities onto our psyches. The belief instinct is as strong as any other governing the organisation of individuals in society.

Dolphins are warm-blooded, breathe air, and suckle their young, as we do. The baby is born in a puff of blood a few metres down, and begins swimming immediately. His mother swims ahead of him, and draws him up in her slipstream to the surface for his first crucial breath, knowing that his instincts are telling him to hold his breath until

---

think that the inevitable conclusion of such a process is extinction. It's a classical conflict between constant and variable energies.

he gets there. His instincts guide him also in the complicated art of feeding. He doesn't suck directly on the pair of nipples situated just ahead of his mother's tail. Instead, he positions himself once again in her slipstream, keeping up close, and she squirts the milk at his mouth. With not much practice, he manages to get more milk than seawater down his gullet.

From the first moment he sees the outside world — "first light" to astronomers — the baby dolphin knows enough to perform all the basics. He holds his breath, swims with good style, and breathes in only when his head is clear of the water. He recognises his mother, and knows where to go to get fed. He hits dolphin-world running; he is born equipped with a written code of conduct in his cells. *Just as we are.* The process of evolution is itself intelligent. It plays itself forward by reacting to challenges and experimenting. Failures are discarded without malice, and successes are encouraged without arrogance. It is bewilderingly complex in its detail, yet astonishingly simple in execution. The aim of evolution is survival of the species. It's one of the primal duality balances, an asymmetry in favour of survival over extinction.

Before we go any further, let me clarify what I mean when I say *evolution*. I use the term in the sense that's implied in physics (physics is famous for stealing English words and giving them hefty makeovers). It refers to the growth of complexity — that is, the opposite of decay into entropy predicted and indeed required by the laws of thermodynamics. It is a bottom-up process, where smaller, simpler creatures interact with one another and with other creatures to form bigger, more complex, cleverer creatures.

I must emphasise that I am not convinced that this is how things work, and in that I have been influenced by South African theoretical physicist George Ellis, who proposes that the development of structure is more likely a top-down process — it's called *emergence* — and there is some compelling observational evidence to support this. The splitting of nations and their territories into successively smaller pockets is direct evidence of increasing entropy. But we digress.

The whole genetic paradigm — its design philosophy, if you will — centres on the mechanical transmission of defining characteristics in such a way that there is a tendency to optimise the recipient offspring. This is patently evolutionary in nature. Why else would it be so? If man was created in a fully evolved state (I modestly decline to employ the adjective "perfect" here), then why on Earth does he have genetically coded reproduction? It allows — nay, *compels* — him to evolve. Each succeeding generation has advantages, however slight, that its ancestors did not. Chromosomes from the parent combine to form a model that goes forward, and the process of natural selection favours those best equipped to cope with their environment. The ongoing genes reflect this. It's not that the Siberian tiger said, "*Gee, it's cold here. Let me grow a nice, thick coat of fur to keep warm.*" In tiger populations in particularly cold habitats, individuals with thicker coats survived in greater numbers than tigers with less fur, and so the gene pool is modified by natural selection.

I'm always puzzled why so many Christians seem to think that evolution is an enemy of Christian theology. I would have thought it more sensible to adjust the doctrine to align it with scientific discovery, but then again, I'm a scientist. As I've stated already, I get peeved with Christian authors who manipulate tenets of science to suggest that science supports the ideology selectively extracted from the chosen scriptures. A good example of this sort of thing is F C Payne's widely read 1945 booklet, *The Seal of God in Creation and the Word*. In it, he asks the question *"Why is it that, although the Jews have circumcised their male children without break for approximately four thousand years, it has not had the slightest effect on their offspring?"* He discusses the matter no further, and treats it as a rhetorical question, incontrovertibly damning of Darwinian evolution.

Payne clearly does not know much about Darwin's evolutionary model, nor has he spent much time studying Siberian tigers. Circumcision does not necessarily change the gene. Like the Siberian tiger, Jewish boys *born* with genetically coded survival advantages would in time dominate the tribe and consequently enrich the gene pool with the code that lets them flourish while those without it wither. Post-natal circumcision may not represent survival privilege — heck, in the case of the Jews, the most persecuted tribe on Earth, it certainly didn't help much at all — and in any case does not rewrite the genome. You can cut my arm off, but my genes will still construct my child with both arms.

We need to clarify the role of conscious thought. What better way to do this than by examining models of conscious thought? The crucial question is how much free will is at play? We have to concentrate on human beings to get the answers to this, but studying lower species is also usefully informative. In our own case, the intelligence of extra-conscious, involuntary functions is absolutely incredible. The entire running of our body's physiology, in all its spectacular intricacy, is done without any help from our egos. In *The Virtue of Heresy*, I touched on this, using the faculty of sight as an example, but there's much more to it. Blood clotting, on its own, is a mind-boggling process. The digestion of food and the utilisation of trapped energy; the passing of complex, detailed information across the synapse of nerve cells; the biochemical utilisation of air in the lungs and ensuing connection to the brain; the chemistry of our livers; our endocrine system; the DNA-RNA dynamic and the manufacture of proteins; the immune system; the contraction of muscles in our hands and arms to facilitate typing these words on a keyboard; the vast behaviour of skin and hair; the influence of instinct — these are just random examples of incredibly complex functions that have no input from our conscious or unconscious thought. They are directed and controlled entirely by the intelligence residing somewhere in our component atoms.[3]

The definition of intelligence is controversial. It's one of those things that drives us bananas because it dances that maddening dance between a visceral conception common to nearly everyone and the vast array of words that can be used to describe it until we lose any rational understanding that we might have had in the first place. In the words of Sir Fred Hoyle, we *"complicate it to the point of incomprehensibility."* Much as I object to semantics, we are going

---

3 Although I shall try my best to precis the wonders of chemistry here, I do urge you to read chapter 6 of *The Virtue of Heresy* to get a more complete picture of the role of atoms in the universe.

to have to attempt a definition of *intelligence* in conversational English.

Intelligence is about evaluating options and making choices. It therefore touches upon the tricky notion of free will, about which we shall argue at length in this book. Intelligence starts with the recognition of a pattern, the setting of that pattern in a particular context, and then acting upon the message thus received — even if the action is no more that the next thought in a series. It's doing because we *want* to do, not because we *have* to. Flowering plants that use biomechanical "muscles" to turn their faces towards the Sun are not demonstrating intelligence. Computers that follow the options presented by machine code are not being intelligent. My looking through the window and deciding because of the miserable weather to watch rugby on television instead of schlepping down to the King's Park stadium is intelligent reasoning.

Perhaps I can throw this in — intelligence requires an ego. The virtual entity that exercises the options must have an identity, and must be able to appreciate subjective motivation like pleasure and pain, love and hate, and disinterest and enthusiasm. The intelligent being does not make the best choices based upon independent, objective analysis. It goes always with the whims of the subjective self, irrespective of how ill-considered they might be. So, the first thing that we can say about intelligence is that it is not very clever.

The principle then is that intelligence rests upon the premise of a sense of self.

The formal arguments around the issue of free will, though confined to a niche group of intense philosophers, explore more the realm of sophistry than cogent argument, in my opinion, and I want to put it to bed right here so we can move on: *The illusion of free will is itself an illusion.*

I have a strong aversion to the reduction of intelligent discourse to the level of semantics. It ruins both the spirit and the letter of useful dialogue, and it's so easy to get lost in words and definitions when talking about free will because the concepts are arcane. One of the stumbling blocks is what exactly constitutes free will. The problem word is *free*.

In the hilarious television comedy series *That '70s Show*, a dialogue between two of the characters (a couple engaged to be married) concerns how best to do the prenuptial shopping, and why the groom prefers to take their friend Jackie with him rather than his fiancée. It goes something like this:

> **Donna**: Eric, I just don't know why you can have more fun with Jackie than with me.

> **Eric**: I don't know, she doesn't ask me questions, she just tells me what to do. It's a strange kind of freedom, but I know why the caged bird sings, Donna.

Let me summarise: Free will, in my book, is the option to make choices in the moment, subject only to biases. Thus, it is self-motivation by an individual that is not the direct, incontrovertible, predetermined command of our design paradigm. In this, we are undoubtedly influenced by instinct's chemically based instruction set, but we can nevertheless still at times make choices that are directly counter-instinctive, for example, to commit suicide. There's an element of randomness to thoughts that gives the lie to notions of strict determinism. I accept that there is such a thing as free will, albeit only relatively so, and my intent is to try to expose how much (or how little) it really influences outcomes for the species.

Consider an ant. Does it have free will? Or does it simply obey a chemical imperative? Individual ants apparently see themselves as mere quanta of the greater social organism. I look at ants a lot; they fascinate me. There's no room for egotism in their psychological makeup, and there is equally no space for democracy. Their obedience to what must seem to them to be their queen, their leader, *their raison d'être*, is absolute and supremely unselfish. She is a benevolent dictator, installed by the divine right of kings.[4] Both she and the quantum-ants demonstrate a pure alignment with their instinct, and here before us lies a powerful lesson: In purely biological terms, in the cold light of evolution, there is no advantage to noble thought.

The ratio in our behaviour — both as individuals and as species — between behaviour determined by our cellular, chemical code, and that resulting from our thoughts and opinions is what interests me more than anything. After years perusing the literature and even more years studying animals, I am led to conclude that the contribution of free will is generally trivial. We do what chemistry tells us

---

4 The queen ant, like the queen bee, is clearly genetically separated as an individual from her minions. She has a bespoke biological function, massaged and fed to realisation by the nursing ants, which sets her apart from the workers and the soldiers. In our species, the design differences are not as clear, although they must exist.

to do, and our conscious contributions seem largely decorative. Sometimes we behave in counter-intuitive ways due to the influence of aberrant chemical instruction, as with drug addiction for example, but these are exceptions rather than the rule.

One of the most lucid, convincing, and indeed, popular figures in the free will debate is charismatic Californian neuroscientist Sam Harris. He is an extremely persuasive talker, with a self-deprecating charm that harmonises perfectly with his boyish good looks and the reassuring timbre of his voice. Dr Harris is a bestselling author in fifteen languages and greatly in demand as a speaker; none of this, however, necessarily makes his thesis correct. You see, Sam Harris argues with zeal that there is no such thing as free will. I disagree.

The summary of his arguments is contained in the readable little booklet that bears the title *Free Will*[5]. It was in that publication that I found the flaws in his model. I must be honest though — Dr Harris and I are not that far apart. It's a question of degree more than principle. Harris would have us believe that free will does not exist in any size, shape or form, and that our behaviour is completely predetermined; to the extent that, in theory at least, scientists can use detectable neurological activity to predict future events with absolute precision. There are no error bars on this imaginary chart. Harris would have us believe that at a cellular, maybe atomic level, our brains in a sense pre-create the future. The brain, if you will, creates the

---

5 Sam Harris, *Free Will* (New York: Free Press, 2012).

event in its own internal cyberspace, independently of our awareness or influence, and then brings that conception to reality in the material world exactly. What's more, as Dr Harris and his cited experimentalists insist, they can measure, with a precision of milliseconds, the delay between the time that the brain creates the event and the advent of the subject's pseudo-intention to perform it. When I'm on the squash court with a wily opponent, these guys are telling me, I'm not really thinking on my feet and planning a clever response to his shots; that's an illusion. Both our strategies are predetermined, like a computer playing chess against a computer. Something inside us is aware of stuff before it happens. Heck, that's almost biblical.

My contention, a thesis put forward in this work, is that free will does indeed exist, but with severely limited scope. Hence, I really am closer to Sam Harris than I am to the Pope. But our point of divergence is crucial; there is a world of difference in concept and execution between one percent free will and zero free will. We do have the ability to evaluate circumstances, both real and imagined.

Harris uses the analogy of a real case of particularly gruesome rape and murder, implying that the perpetrators had no choice in the matter and were essentially blameless. He suggests that the cellular impulse is irresistible, or that a person has no faculty to countermand an extra-conscious imperative in a certain way.

I dispute this. We do, for example, have a moral compass. We can make choices between base acts and sober behaviour. Think about it. We constrain ourselves, use etiquette, and take into consideration the feelings of others. That is how we maintain civilised society. The exceptions are aberrations. We are not driven by a complete sense of hedonism; we practice constraint. I have many times experienced a crisis of conscience, and I'm sure you have too. We vacillate between opposing courses of action, sometimes crumbling and going with base urges which we may later regret, and sometimes retaining moral integrity and choosing a less primitive path.

We could add here that drugs play a role — alcohol frequently lowers our inhibitions and causes us to behave recklessly, with often dire consequences. In simple terms, the bad behaviour consequent to being drunk was not itself free will as we have defined it here, but the choice to take the alcohol in the first place was. So clearly, the influence of will — willpower, if you like — can be eroded by circumstances, in the manner that a prisoner of war being tortured for treacherous information weighs his moral duty to secrecy against the pain of losing another fingernail. We can be driven to make bad decisions by illness or malady. When the theatre of choices ultimately loses all rational constraint, the person is clinically insane.

My vision of free will is more closely aligned with that of Tufts University philosophy professor and bestselling author Daniel C. Dennett. In his 1978 work *Brainstorms*, [6] Dr Dennett puts it thus:

> The model of decision making I am proposing has the following feature: when we are faced with an important decision, a consideration-generator whose

---

6 Daniel C. Dennett, *Brainstorms: Philosophical Essays on Mind and Psychology* (Boston: MIT Press, 1981), chap. 15.

output is to some degree undetermined produces a series of considerations, some of which may of
course be immediately rejected as irrelevant by the
agent (consciously or unconsciously). Those considerations that are selected by the agent as having
a more than negligible bearing on the decision then
figure in a reasoning process, and if the agent is in
the main reasonable, those considerations ultimately
serve as predictors and explicators of the agent's final
decision.

He goes on to list the reasons why his model works better than the opposition's, but his style of expression is a
little too abstruse for a verbatim quote to be useful here. Dr
Dennett's points can be reduced to more easily digestible
language. Essentially, a human being can make choices.
We have an internal faculty that produces a range of
options when we are faced with an important focal point in
our lives, and we have the ability to prioritise those options,
rejecting some outright, and bringing others into play in
the concluding money-or-the-box decision.

The final decision is our choice, free in the sense that
we are not compelled to make it. We choose a particular
forward path because we *want* to, based on the information — conscious or unconscious — that we have to hand.
Dennett puts intelligence into its rightful place, in my view,
and in so doing, helps to define it. It is important also, that
Dennett — an atheist — remains conscious always of the
moral parapet from which we launch decisions. In a few
words, Dr Dennett is proposing partially free choices, and
that suits me well.

We can plan actions hours, days, even years ahead. In our mind's eye, we can imagine a scenario, commit that intention to memory, and in due course bring that choice to pass if the will remains. I suppose Harris is saying that the act of planning is preordained, but how could he or anyone else possibly know this? This mirrors the tantalising image of Hilton the quantum mechanic proving by the power of his mental processes that he does not exist.

Not all behavioural motivations are delivered from somewhere in our atoms. Neurologists may have a model of what they *think* constitutes *thought*, but it cannot be empirically verified. This parallels the idea of black holes in cosmology — the model suggests a certain radiation signature for black holes, so the assumption is made that wherever that signature is more or less matched in observation, there must without doubt be a cleverly concealed black hole causing it. We can't see black holes (they are by definition invisible) any more than we could peer into another's brain and examine his thoughts. With current and foreseeable technology, neither of these observations is possible. What we do get — and it's a magnificent achievement, I'll give you that — is a radiation signature of neural activity. Interpreting that as a detailed and readable image of thought is yet another misleading effect of belief.

All you need for free will to function is the ability to resist suggestions from instinct. You do not, as Harris suggests, need *"to be aware of all the factors that determine your thoughts and actions, and to have complete control over those factors.*"[7] In short, you need willpower. In order to have willpower, you must have opinions, and opinions are a manifestation of belief. Our personalities are the net outcome of the conflict between belief and instinct, and if both sides are functioning properly, we present as reasonably coherent people.

We develop opinions, and these weight the forward projection of thoughts. It's a simple association of data values. Sensory input flows into our data processor, and output is computed with a set of biases, both personal and global. These include, *inter alia*, memory of past events, intuition and instinct, genetic influences, and external stimuli (pleasure and pain). The forward and lateral projection of thoughts is simply a weighted trend. The reaction of the individual results from a combination of all these influences and personal will is weighed against the bias expressed in our cells. Thus, free will is never free in the sense that it is not subject to influence; but if the chemical command is "turn left", the possibility exists that we'll see a right turn. There are subtle forces at play, and free will is actually real and distinct from purely instinctive preconception.

I have a kitten named Misty. She teaches me a lot. The other day, she produced for my edification and delight a lizard's tail, separated from its rightful owner and twitching this way and that in hopeless protest. It recalled horrific childhood scenes of a headless chicken leaping around and flapping its wings in a grotesque death dance. Just as I did then, I wondered how the lizard was getting its severed tail

---

7 Sam Harris, *Free Will* (New York: Free Press, 2012).

to behave like that. It was disconnected from the brain, and operated independently of any type of conscious instruction as far as I could tell. What struck me was the motion. Wagging a tail or flapping a wing or kicking the legs are all fairly complex compound sets of neural instructions, applied in a definite sequence. I am cautiously approaching a definition of intelligence here.

You have the chemical elements comprising the families of atoms, and you have models that suggest ways that elements might have formed from pockets of energy by dumb chance and with no particular preferred direction or evolutionary path. The next step in explaining the universe in a rationally pleasing way is a quantum leap. We have an atom of hydrogen and an atom of oxygen, and if we ignore their inherent complexity, we can happily accept that they came about by accident over an awfully long period of time. What then causes these two lonely souls to react with one another, and what constrains that reaction so that it is always the same for given ambient conditions? What template defines their form so that they might reproduce themselves exactly?

Can you see where I'm going? The plan must have preceded the progeny. It's the egg ...

It is at once both interesting and confounding to ponder the origin of instinct. Could this para-intelligent appreciation of the ultimate purpose of a living being have evolved alongside formation of the first working, physical model in that species? I just can't see it.

Another really fascinating aspect of this for me is a future projection in my imagination: What happens if this design strategy is so successful that our species in due course outweighs its usefulness to the world? What happens when the creep of human civilisation, pressed unmercifully onwards by sheer weight of numbers, depletes the rain forests' CO_2 lungs to such an extent that we no longer have enough oxygen to breathe? Will our free will turn against our instinct? Will we be compelled by population pressure to rebel against the primal cellular code? Is it conceivable that noble thoughts will foment a revolution and direct us away from the floundering ant heap in which we would no doubt ultimately suffocate? Will we be led from our divine destiny by a drunken piper and go as lemmings over a cliff?

And even more sobering for me is that we are there already.

Whether we humans are the product of design, as I believe we must be, or grand artefacts of a fantastic, aimless, ongoing chemical reaction called evolution is irrelevant to the point I'm trying to make, which is that we are merely pawns in the game. Either way, we are prisoners of the primordial instruction set that defines our species and the way it behaves. Sadly, the rudder of free will has inflexible stops a degree or two either side of dead ahead, if you'll pardon the pun.

One of the most significant principles of natural selection proposed by Darwin was the concept of intra-special competition. Effective enhancements to species come about not through vying with other species, but because of competition with members of the *same* species. This principle has a deep chemical root, and it was graphically illustrated nearly a century later when Robert Ardrey put forward his thesis on territory.

We can model evolution mathematically to study the maturation of code, and in fact, the whole process by which science advances is evolutionary. The crucial difference, of course, between natural organic evolution and the advance of structured, systematic knowledge lies in the intervention of intelligence. The branch of mathematics called *statistics* didn't evolve naturally from simple environmental needs. Geometry and trigonometry did. Every year, the ancient Egyptians had to accurately divide the shifting agricultural patchwork along the banks of the Nile, and triangulation was the way to do it. By contrast, however, the applied science of identifying patterns in sets of numbers, and using these to predict probable future configurations was the brainchild of John Graunt, a seventeenth-century London haberdasher. His inquisitive but scientifically untrained mind led him to ponder what we might learn from the way that people died. After closing his tiny needles-and-pins shop in the evenings, Graunt would sit in the warm glow of an oil lamp and ponder the mysteries of the bills of mortality kept by the morgues of greater London.

What he managed to extrapolate from those documents laid the foundations of actuarial science, and provided the basis of the business of life insurance. John Graunt was later to be honoured by admission to the Royal Society by the decree of no less than Charles the Second himself. There was more to it, however. By drawing attention to anatomical details of a substantial sample of the human population as it was some four hundred years ago, Graunt has given us an invaluable glimpse of how Homo sapiens has evolved physically during that time. On the evolutionary time scale, four hundred years is a blink of an eye, but the measurable changes that have occurred are tremendously important to the calibration of phylogeny.

However, and I'd like to underline this, we have the innate ability — the skill set, if you like — to act with compassion and philanthropy. In our quiver of motivational arrows, they are there, no less significant than those antisocial traits like cruelty and torture. Which path we choose may well be influenced by strong chemical biases, and this is why we have laws and jurisprudence. The legal system, in its essence, really expresses a desire for decency in our social behaviour. That some parties bend this to their own nefarious ends is also part of our design. It's quite natural, but that doesn't mean I like it. So we *can* make a difference, but it's a social analgesic, masking the pain only locally in space and time, and with no long-lasting effect. Here we are getting close to the bone in uncovering the role of individuals within the smothering organic tribe.

What we have is a classical case of constant and variable forces interacting. We can reuse the old analogy of throwing a ball up into the air — the variable kinetic energy of momentum carries it upwards against the constant mass energy of gravitation pulling it downwards. As the momentum decreases, the ball slows down until the two forces equal out, and then it begins to accelerate back towards the Earth. Our cellular code is a constant, unvarying influence on our lives, whereas our free choice washes with the tides. Oh yes, we will fight the good fight, but only until we tire of it and grow hungry or scared or cold; then we will return unabashed to the hand that threw us out there in the first place. It's no big deal.

There does appear to be a linear progression to our evolution, although of course, that's the same kind of illusion that makes it seem as if the Sun goes around the Earth or that the Earth is irrevocably warming or that time is a linear series of values that grows ever longer by the addition of new events. Our tunnel vision limits itself to a small part of the curve. We don't have wide-angle eyes to see the other side of the wave. That is what history and technology should show us, but both invariably distort the image. What *is* linear is the evolution of technology, and I suppose that is the badge of knowledge. The question really is, has human thought and disposition improved over the span of time in which such things were recorded?

We could try to take as reference points selected events in prominent epochs in recorded history, and see if they can represent human thought in a way that a trend line can be superimposed on the curve. Looking back, we see that marvellous era of classical Greek philosophy that led to the formulation of democracy amongst other great achievements in human thinking. It was Socrates himself, some four hundred years BC, who coined the name and the field of ethics. Compared with the purity of their thoughts, can we really assert that standards of Greek society have improved from that time to this? In my judgement, it has gone backwards.

Then we could consider the appearance of Jesus, and the years leading to the posthumous transformation of his philosophy into Christianity. Is contemporary Christian ethos an improvement on what it was at origin? Or is it subjectively worse, more divided, and increasingly prone to aberrations and false prophets?

In the field of science, is it possible that anyone could believe that the philosophical morality maintained by Isaac Newton is surpassed by contemporary thinkers? Is the scientist of today less or more greedy and self-interested than Newton's contemporaries were?

We could go on and on. Is modern-day Peru better, in a moral sense, than it was under their ancestral Incas? How does the morality of Neanderthals — or even gorillas, for that matter — stack up against the habits of modern-day Europe? There may be specific peaks and valleys in the wave of social mores over the centuries, but to my mind, the trend is clearly down.

Nevertheless, in a frame of reference that's limited to the last two or three thousand years, we can make some useful projections of our future on the planet. As a biologist friend said over lunch the other day, we are now able to see the evolution of the gene itself, a maturation of the code, and it is happening fairly rapidly (quickly enough for measurable changes to the code in fifty elapsed years). How significant this is, I don't know, given that genetically, we are nearly identical to primates, and very, very similar even to bacteria. But I suspect that we are still constrained by the basics of the code that defines our species, and slightly more broadly, defines all living things. We can learn a lot about those constraints by studying less-sophisticated species. How do different species adapt to changes in their environment? In the 1970s, the docudrama *The Hellstrom Chronicle* (a story about competition for the world about us) created a buzz in cinemas around the world. The fictional narrator, biologist Nils Hellstrom, uttered the following memorable line: "*Human beings compete for the world by trying to adapt the environment to suit themselves; insects do it by adapting themselves to suit the environment. Insects will win."*

Why did democracy succeed where communism failed? Because it caters to the ignoble reality inherently in our nature (self-interest and greed) where the Marxist ideal is an unnatural utopia of fine thought (all men are equal and want to share their wealth). Put another way: Democracy and its economic system, capitalism, represent freedom, while Marxism and communism are synonymous with control and oppression. All regimes are held by forceful control of the sycophantic populace, but the communists require it more — a lot more — than the democrats. The Berlin Wall was to stop people following their wish to go to the West, not to stop the West from going East. The more unnatural the philosophy, the more draconian the law of arms required to protect it from enlightenment.

There may be a linear trend, but I fear it is not one which leads us towards a noble utopian conclusion. The trend I see is increasing conflict: the wash of globalisation, the blurring of boundaries, and the weakening of bulwarks between tribes and between nations versus the primitive need for tribal turf. It is socialism without the anchor of doctrine. I am literally afraid. The smearing of the fractal nature of human society flies in the face of fundamental instinctive imperatives. Without them, there is the stark possibility that Homo sapiens will plunge into its ultimate inevitable extinction not by pollution or war, but by unconstrained, torrential insanity. The human race will go mad and die.

This immediately raises some alarming caveats — how do we ascertain and quantify for comparison the state of human thought? This is one of the greatest obstacles to progress in both the humanities and in physical science. In order to find a trend, we need first to measure and establish data points. We saw how patently difficult this can be in the testing of anthropogenic global warming theory. How do you take the Earth's temperature, for heaven's sake? There is after all no convenient orifice in which we can insert our global thermometer. How do we establish the data points in the quality of human thought?

We should not neglect the value we ascribe to our own beliefs. How many times have we heard someone say, "I am Roman Catholic (or Republican or Greenpeace or Wiccan, whatever) and *proud* of it." Why should we be proud? Does our opinion on some element of reality raise us above the rabble? This is something worth thinking about — the reward we feel from belonging is a manifestation of the territorial imperative. It demonstrates the conversion of our opinions into convictions, driven by a primal instinct. The process is simple, but the detail can at times seem bewildering.

We have some rather odd ways of expressing ourselves. Take the very interesting and relevant concept issue of pollution, for example. Pollution ties together the expression of basic survival needs and overt sanctimoniousness. When we add moral high ground to our projection of self, we depart from the rational and enter the realm of pure, instinct-driven behaviour. Clinically, pollution describes a change in the chemistry of our environment, such that it alters the course of ecology. Yet we view it selectively, and filter it with insufferable sanctimoniousness. By what wildly deviant standard of logic could we possibly believe that wind farms are not pollution? These bristling towers of steel and plastic and deadly poisonous metals, with their invasive, psychotic "black noise", to say nothing of their gross violation of the aesthetics of nature, are considered eco-friendly? The environmental cleanliness of wind turbines goes just as far as the wind striking the fan; from there on, it is pollution at every imaginable level. What peculiar people we are.

It may seem odd that I have included a discussion on pollution, but as we shall soon see, the topic is intensively integrated into the sociopolitical mindset. The relevance of pollution seemed obvious at first, simply an extension of domestic hygiene, yet I grew to understand that it had far more profound implications. Arguments about pollution are zealous, and entitle the person opposing it to don a cloak named "righteous indignation". Concern about perceived threats to the environment in most cases far exceeds its factual base, and is somewhat pompously considered to be a moral high ground. But is it?

Why should we care about what happens to the Earth after we are dead? We'll be dead after all, and beyond caring, not so? Yet there is something deep down in our subconscious being that makes what we leave behind feel important to us. We are instinctively driven to protect our own lives, and we may deduce from that impulse that it is essential, for some reason held higher than our intellect, to remain alive. We don't react to sudden threats by figuring them out. We instinctively and immediately protect ourselves. It would appear, if you will pardon my surprise, that independently of any intellectual considerations, our paltry lives have a *higher purpose*.

Why should this be so? Our individual lifespan is so short in the scheme of things, and our contribution to the running of the universe so infinitesimally trivial that it seems almost ludicrous that we hold such a passionate aversion to our own demise. Dying is no big deal, yet we abhor it. Bees don't suffer from this phobia; nor do ants. The individuals in those tribes seem immune to the human's tendency to exaggerate his own value to the universal plan. In other words, they seem to be blessed with an ability to see their egos to scale.

> Perhaps the best cure for the fear of death is to reflect that life has a beginning as well as an end. There was a time when you were not: that gives us no concern. Why then should it trouble us that a time will come when we shall cease to be? To die is only to be as we were before we were born.
>
> William Hazlitt, essayist (1778–1830)

It is difficult to be logical about the importance of our own instincts. Let's face it, they were not rationally obtained, nor were they a matter of choice. At no stage did we check little boxes in the prenatal set-up programme to design our visceral selves. Our instincts are intrinsically part of our greater being, that superego that owns our conscious identity. There can be few things more delicious than loving sex, and this is crucial — the "love" aspect of copulation makes it vastly more satisfying than any other motivation we might have to perform the act. Loveless sex inevitably requires artificial enhancement — gymnastics, role-playing, drugs, promiscuity, and so on — to keep it on the boil; love-full sex does not, or at least, not to the same degree. It transcends in no small measure the delight we might experience by merely stimulating nerve ends, and once again, I ask myself, why? Clearly, it is an instinctive imperative designed to encourage the longer-term bonding of a sexual couple, and therefore, it seems to me, it is aimed at more successful propagation of the species and improved nurturing of its offspring. I'm sorry to say this, my fellow romantics, but "love" is just the fragrance embellishing an otherwise run-of-the-mill chemical reaction. Damn.

So where does pollution come into the equation? It's an expression of the meaning of life. Philosophical and religious arguments aside, what is our purpose as individuals? Why are we alive, and what is it that our design paradigm is so determined for us to achieve individually that it gives us almost irresistibly enticing chemical instructions to stay alive as long as we possibly can, and to copulate more enthusiastically and with less regard to cost than just about anything else we do? It must be for propagation of the species. Nothing else makes sense. We are designed as ants in the organic colony, protecting our persons with mindless vigour so that ultimately we play a role that is no more, at best, than an infinitesimal shove in the backside of our species. Like the ant, we then die, breaking down into chemicals that reseed the environment, but unlike the ant, we are damned unhappy about the prospect.

Our aversion to pollution is thus an instinctive mindset, part of our dedication to the survival of our species expressed as caring about how nurturing the environment will be for survivors after we've done our bit. It is not "moral or "ethical", but just a part of our design that we can take no credit for whatsoever. And yet we do. "Green" and "moral conscience" seem inseparable in the global mindset, at least amongst the well-fed liberals who wave those particular flags. They appear to me to be either completely oblivious to the scale and depth of real human suffering, or to be using the brand of environmental compassion to mask more sinister political goals. Either way, it is an anti-humanist podium upon which they preach. The human animal is defiled in their policy, as if we are somehow unnatural and undeserving of a place on Earth. Let me then propose this: Ignoring for now how frequently these may occur, make a list of all the qualities of thought and attitude that we would consider virtuous, or derived from some higher, more advanced plane of consciousness. Our list would likely include compassion, philanthropy, appreciation of the aesthetic, love, territorial amity, art, forgiveness, aversion to taking life, sympathy, charity, and so on. It is immediately apparent that these virtues are scarce in human society, but let me ask you this — out of all the diversity of living things on our precious planet, what species practices these things more than any other, by an enormous margin? That's right. Good old Homo sapiens, that's who. So give us some credit, will you?

War is not inhuman. It is the most human, the most archetypal of all our varied flavours of social expression. Territorial conflict defines us as a species. This may seem like a profoundly cynical view to you, but one has to be realistic. We are machines of conflict, hard-wired to compete at all costs. We're not ever going to stop competing and taking more than the basic essentials if they are available to us; it is the very foundation upon which we develop.

The only thing that lets me laugh and find satisfaction in a situation like this is the company of those few aberrant genes that cause noble ideals rather than instinctive greed to steer individual behaviour. Yes we are islands, threatened on every side, but heck, Mr President, cut us some slack. We're also children of the universe, you know, subject to all the frailties of our species.

The question before the human race is, whether the God of Nature shall govern the world by his own laws, or whether priests and kings shall rule it by fictitious miracles?

JOHN ADAMS, SECOND PRESIDENT
OF THE UNITED STATES, 1785

No matter what my personal beliefs may or may not be, I have always maintained that religion has no place in science. Faith in God has its own place, and its own way of exploring reality to find meaning. Indeed, I have no problem with religionists using science as an element in their internal debates—provided of course that they do not twist the science to fit their argument. But the reverse is patently unacceptable to me. Science is secular and should remain independent of any and all theological models

8

THE WORLD ACCORDING
TO HAWKING

The vanishing hole in our socks

STEPHEN HAWKING IS AN icon. The painfully slumped, wasted, rag-doll figure, head lolling almost catatonically to one side; the robotic voice-over that transposes his fantastic thoughts into human speak; and a sardonic, self-deprecating sense of humour that rises and cheers from the ashes of his torment: these qualities characterise one of the heroic frontiersmen of human intellectual exploration. The courage of the man is staggering. He has coped with a yoke of adversity that would have broken the spirit of lesser mortals, and has been nothing less than an inspiration to a footloose generation that survived the trepidation of new-millennium superstition. Dr Hawking is a fragile asset in this belligerent world, and he deserves our boundless respect and admiration.

If anyone on planet Earth needs their full capacity for communication, it's Stephen Hawking. Possibly the greatest mind to emerge in the twentieth century, Dr Hawking showed little interest in the frivolous pursuits of his peers; he had the gift of mathematical genius, and he lived to express those fugues of calculus for the benefit of mankind. Yet, in an unbelievably cruel flutter of fate, his ability to share his thoughts was taken from him, practically all of it. Muscular dystrophy wrapped its cold tentacles around Dr Hawking in his early twenties, and with taunting deliberateness, slowly deprived him of all conscious control of his muscles, until only his eyes were left. Everything he says to an eagerly waiting world, every word, every sum, every thought, he bequeaths to us by blinking.

Could any of us, even those trained to a razor's edge in rare, high-altitude mathematics, possibly imagine in what splendid isolation swims the island mind of Stephen Hawking? He can move not a finger for himself, cannot feed himself, nor comb his hair, or brush his teeth, yet he can solve nonlinear, partial differential equations in his *mind*. Without writing any of it down, he finds a workable solution, and then checks it. Finally, in the ultimate demonstration of almost superhuman mental agility, he must communicate the solution thus obtained — a set of equations set in mathematical symbols too arcane for me to write on this page — to his personal assistant by *blinking*. This is a man who cannot move a finger.

And yet, I will solemnly declare, he foists the most incredible nonsense upon our brave new world. Dr Hawking, I am here with my hat in my hand to inform you that your thesis is nothing more than psychedelic mumbo jumbo: twenty-first-century snake oil sucked in with unseemly haste by a bewildered, fatal tribe. Those who click on your icon, I submit, are entering a cyber-gaming world where the garden path leads not to enlightenment, but to a phantom paradise where nothing is real and where we can waste our lives in splendidly wanton seclusion.

Theoretical physicists are a strange bunch. Like some of the products they give issue to, figuring out just what it is that they are is an unavoidable but tiresome overhead to interaction with modern physics. Let's cut to the chase — theoretical physicists are metamathematicians. They are people who are convinced, and who try to convince the rest of us, that mathematical constructs are the only way in which reality can be properly understood. In their minds, the mathematical description supersedes our experiential interaction with nature. And believe me, they are incorrigible. They brook no dissent, and that's that. It took me a long time to untangle the causal roots of their dogma, and eventually I settled on this: Because of their training — conditioning, if you will — they are simply incapable of solving problems any other way. Their way is not simply the best way; I hear them say it's the *only* way.

The impact of this mindset is devastating. It became apparent to me while trying to practice astronomy and astrophysics. I noticed something strange. All the theoretical physicists I came in contact with, no matter where they were or what they did for a living, were also cosmologists. And vice versa, even more strictly: there has not been a cosmologist in the last one hundred years who was not also a theoretical physicist. Observational astronomers were excluded from cosmology unless they were also *au fait* with theoretical physics. This is extremely important to the matter in hand. In practice, there is no difference between a theoretical physicist and a cosmologist, and we can take that one step further: They are, in the cold light of day, both just barely disguised metamathematicians who test their equations on conceptual models of unreachable stars. There is a very good reason for this. If the observed system is far enough away, no one can argue. The equation is law. Galaxy superclusters must bow to that, and so must we. Therein lies the rub.

Stephen Hawking turned 71 on January 8th, 2014. He once held the Lucasian Chair of Mathematics at Cambridge University, under what I would imagine to be the disapproving ghostly glare of Sir Isaac Newton, who had occupied that very same seat some three hundred years earlier. How different they are. Newton was the archetypal detached, reclusive, muttering seventeeth-century professor, given more to theology than physics, more to alchemy than biochemistry. He put forward, in utterly brilliant simplicity, a system of mechanics that describes a clockwork universe so precisely that his equations are used to this day to plot the flight paths of interplanetary space probes and to calculate the mass of atomic particles.

His innovations were profoundly useful and led to immense, exponentially accelerating progress in physical science. They included even the invention of differential calculus to enable the calculation of quantities at astronomical and atomic extremes. Despite Newton's lifelong obsession with "magick", his analysis of the world was, to a fault, without any hint of the supernatural. He was a cranky loner, bad-tempered, a terribly bad communicator; he had no wish for fame in an academic sphere he considered irrevocably broken, and it was only intervention by his long-suffering friend Edmond Halley that brought New-ton's landmark *Principia Mathematica* to publication. In addition to all this, he was an astronomer, in the purest sense of the word.

Stephen Hawking is in every respect Newton's polar opposite. He belongs to that select class of pop stars that first hit the media radar in the early 1900s with the launch of Einstein's relativity — the celebrity scientist. Albert Einstein cast the mould for a whole new breed of player on the stage of science. As mass media developed from print to moving picture, people demonstrated in a far more discernible way their tendency to hero-worship individuals who are popular. The interesting aspect of this is that the adulation is not correlated with an informed appreciation of their idol's true talent. The network born out of global information media formed virtual tribes long before the Internet was created, and they were grouped, then as now, around some common focus point. That focus in the early days of the media revolution was usually a person.

It is by now well known that with the publication in 1915 of Einstein's second mind-boggling theory, no more than a handful of extremely focussed mathematicians in the whole world could decipher the almost impossibly eso-teric mathematical dialect (called *differential geometry*) in which general relativity theory was couched. Incredibly, Einstein himself could not understand it, and delegated the task of constructing the mathematical formalism to his friend Professor Marcel Grossmann at the University of Berlin. The earlier special relativity had already whet pub-lic appetite, to an extent unprecedented in history.

Despite the consuming cataclysm of the First World War raging all around them, Western minds lit up at the prospect of an incarnated mystic about to tell tales of the great beyond. German astronomer Karl Schwarzschild famously sent Einstein a letter containing his solution to the equations of Einstein's general relativity theory, which led in due course to the popular concept of cosmological black holes. The letter was mailed from an icy trench on the Russian front, some six weeks before Schwarzschild perished there.

Shortly after the conclusion of hostilities, Sir Arthur Eddington was commissioned to lead an expedition to the tropics to observe the 1919 solar eclipse and bring back observational proof of Einstein's controversial theory. When he returned in triumph to England with data that closer examination would later prove had holes in its socks, no one cared what the intricacies of the theory were, nor indeed worried about inconsistencies in Eddington's "evidence". The reception was hysterical. Albert Einstein had been baptised by popular fire. He was well and truly a scientific rock star. He became a household name, an acclaimed celebrity whose iconic shaggy visage is universally recognised, and whose declaration $E = mc^2$ is the best known — and by implication, the most widely misunderstood — item of mathematical formalism in the whole wide world. And the masses who cheered so loudly had not the foggiest notion, not the faintest clue, what his theory meant or how it worked. They just *believed*.

Fast forward seventy years. In 1988, the booklet *A Brief History of Time* was published for a hung-over generation in the hungry, post-psychedelic world, and from out of nowhere, Stephen Hawking exploded upon us. No one outside of academia, and certainly very few besides the closeted, insulated, secret empire of metamathematicians had ever heard of him. Suddenly, he was everywhere; a remote but oh-so-cool mind doing nought but thinking and spewing electronic code that morphed into the gospel of the New Age. I can clearly remember the first time I saw an image of Stephen Hawking, not yet nearly so badly crippled thirty years ago as he is today, but still physically broken enough to qualify as pure mind. I was both intrigued and dazzled. What could possibly have been more appealing to someone like that naive, idealistic, much younger me, an intellectual nincompoop whose deepest, darkest desire was to prove — using the sacred script of quantum mechanics, no less — that I didn't exist. Hawking was my man!

A *Brief History of Time* went on to sell significantly more than ten million copies and netted Dr Hawking both fame and fortune. No one bar a few disenchanted figures in the mathematical underworld dared argue with him; in any case, as with relativity, no one understood and no one cared. He was canonised by eager sycophants, and from that moment on, Hawking could do no wrong. I should have seen it coming, but I didn't. It would take another twenty years of head beating for objective reality to sink in.

Although he has been officially labelled an astronomer (something, I must say, which rather offends me) and even — good grief — a *physicist*, Hawking has always been no more and no less than a mathematician. Perhaps we have a clue here. Speaking in convoluted differential equations brings enlightenment to Dr Hawking no more than a command of Latin would endow a Catholic priest with divine understanding. I'll tell you what it *does* do however, and the explanation fits the good padre who speaks in tongues as well: It makes communication with the rest of us very difficult indeed. So much so that most of us give up trying, and then, if we like those idolised mystics enough to accept their authority, we simply swallow what they're saying as privileged truth.

Scientific endeavour is becoming less and less successful. The trend over the past century or so is alarming if we can bring ourselves to look at the statistics. Leaving aside philosophical histrionics, we measure the success of science ultimately by its ability to produce things that are useful. By useful, I do not mean only unprecedented articles of technology; included are theories which are classified as useful in that they enable the exploration of new ground from which innovation can extract real benefit. It can be as pure as knowledge alone, as long as the knowledge is of real things in our measurable environment. Figments of imagination don't count; that's of use to art, not science. And whilst I love art as much as anyone I know, I keep it apart from the practice of science. As long as it remains imagined, it is imagination; when it comes into the material common reality and does work, it can legitimately be called science.

In a nutshell, science practiced properly is weighed by the benefits it brings. Good science, in my book, influences reality. Concepts that remain exclusively in the mental domain are not yet useful, and their goodness remains moot, no matter how much they form self-supporting closed loops within their rhetorical architecture.

Only when science distils from ideas some practical assistance to the social aims of the tribe can it be called good. Thus, I propose that science becomes science only if and when it is tested against reality *and* produces a usefully applicable result. Until then, it is at best pre-science, existing in the mind as an unblooded model or an untried method.

Early in his career at Cambridge, Stephen Hawking teamed up with eminent theorist Roger Penrose to produce mathematical tools to broaden the range of general relativity (whether they achieved that or not is a moot point, I fear). That may well be the closest he ever came to producing something that helps our world to progress to a better place, inasmuch as general relativity theory can be used to calculate gravitational effects. I must add though, that on scales where the usefulness bears tangible fruit, such as in devising flight paths for interplanetary spacecraft, general relativity theory produces answers no different from Newtonian mechanics, while the latter offers far more user-friendly mathematics. But we needn't concern ourselves too much with that debate right now, because it's what Hawking did next that's relevant. He went the other way exactly, on a direct course away from objective reality, and into the bizarre, irrational world of black holes. And that's where he has remained to this day.

Please bear with me while I make a précis of Hawking's achievements. It's not terribly exciting, but it is crucial for the purposes of the current work that we examine the knowledge he has bestowed upon our poor, long-suffering world. Penrose and Hawking showed us in their calculations that singularities (mass with zero external dimensions) are common occurrences in general relativity, and that, quantum effects aside, the whole universe must have sprung from infinite density and energy.

I can see your eyebrows shooting up at the cavalier treatment of infinity in their model, but don't bail out yet. We'll get through this together. After his initial efforts with Penrose, Hawking applied those tools to the notion of black holes — mathematical constructs so extreme in every respect that were they to exist in reality, they would exert ultragravitation of such magnitude that not even light could escape their clutches. They would consequently be invisible. And, one presumes, voracious.

Hawking's first achievement was proving (mathematically, of course) a theorem by theorist John Wheeler which stated that a black hole could be described by just three parameters — mass, angular momentum, and electrical charge.

Next, he formulated an analogue to the standard laws of thermodynamics that would apply to black holes, solving the until-then vexing problem that black holes seemed to violate the second law of thermodynamics. These creatures were slowly gaining respectability.

Hawking then discovered, according to the solutions he was deriving, that the area of a black hole never decreases. This has implications for entropy, and he was left with the conundrum that if a black hole has entropy, then it also has temperature, which means it would present a radiation image. black holes would no longer be black.

It was at this juncture that Hawking manifested his greatest triumph — he showed that black holes could in fact radiate without being seen. They do so by means of a

postulated quantum trickle, appropriately called Hawking
radiation, which is now cast in stone in the annals of relativity theory. He tells us that at the event horizon of the
black hole, space is not empty. In fact, it is filled with
pairs of virtual particles, that is, particles and antiparticles
conjoined across the event horizon. In a "normal" scenario, the pairs would instantaneously self-annihilate and
disappear, but in Hawking's movie, one is trapped and its
terrible twin (the one *outside* the boundary) escapes. In
January 2014, Dr Hawking posted an essay in *Nature* that
suggested that event horizons are in fact not allowed by
quantum mechanics, which essentially invalidates not
only Hawking radiation, but indeed even black holes
themselves. Of that, more later; it would be decades
before he allowed that level of scepticism to creep in.

I'm not sure if Dr Hawking was getting bored at this
stage, but he started to become sidetracked around about
now, and began to ponder the consequences of add-
ing *information* to a black hole. What would happen to
information if it passed the event horizon? I'll say this for
him: He puts his money where his mouth is. He in 1997
famously entered into a three-way bet with Kip Thorne
and John Preskill. Kip and Stephen were on one side, and
John opposed them.

The issue stemmed from the worrying fact that black
hole theory was paradoxical and represented a direct
conflict between two holy cows of theoretical physics —
general relativity and quantum mechanics. Thorne and
Hawking argued that since general relativity defined black
holes such that it was impossible for them to radiate, and
thereby lose information, the information (that is, the

mass energy) carried by Hawking radiation could not possibly originate from inside the black hole event horizon. As this contradicts the principle of microcausality in quantum mechanics, it is quantum mechanics that needs to be rewritten to accommodate the black hole model.

Preskill argued against the pair, insisting that because quantum mechanics determines that the information emitted by a black hole comes from mass energy inside the event horizon, the model of black holes given by Hawking using general relativity is wrong and must be modified to accommodate the quantum mechanics solution. In 2004, Hawking conceded the bet, and publicly presented Preskill — an Englishman no doubt properly disdainful of American sport — with a baseball encyclopaedia. That was the end of the matter. Thorne never agreed, and Hawking went on to develop theoretical sub-models supporting the view that black holes do after all radiate particles from within their event horizon.

What puzzles me, given the theme of this book, is that the position later adopted by Hawking invalidates the basis of Hawking radiation, yet it is still incorporated within the body of theory taught to physics undergraduates at universities. I suppose it's a manifestation of what I have termed "faith drag".

Then, in a surprise move, Stephen Hawking put his cosmology into reverse. He teamed up with Jim Hartle of the University of California to develop a model that had no boundary in space-time. In a nutshell, he said that the universe is eternal and had no beginning, essentially abandoning the Big Bang model he had defended so ardently against Sir Fred Hoyle in earlier years.

Try as I might, I cannot think of anything really useful, and therefore anything I would classify as good science, in the output of Dr Stephen Hawking over the entire span of his career. One of the finest intellects currently on the planet gave it his best shot for more than half a century, became world famous, acquired enormous wealth, is adored and defended by millions, is recognised and respected in the farthest corners of the globe, and for what? It's a shocking realisation, but based upon what he has produced during his lifetime, Dr Hawking is one of the most ineffectual scientists in living memory. Why is this?

It is certainly not because he is stupid; he is in fact exceptionally intelligent. He has courage, passion, and integrity. So why couldn't he cure cancer or invent a revolutionary telescope or devise a way to more efficiently explore the moons of Saturn? To be quite honest, it is not in the least because he was not capable of doing those things. It is, I submit, because of the method he was trained to use. His conscription to the mathematics of imagination sucked him into a vortex that sustains itself indefinitely without need of physical interaction with reality.

In a stunning turnaround quite unanticipated when I began writing this book, Stephen Hawking himself suddenly threw the whole issue onto its head. In January 2014, just as I was preparing the manuscript for print, Dr Hawking dropped a bombshell in the form of a paper published in *Nature*. He titled it *Information Preservation and Weather Forecasting for Black Holes*, and in the concluding paragraphs Stephen Hawking states the following:

> I take this as indicating that … there would be no
> event horizons and no firewalls. *The absence of event
> horizons means that there are no black holes* — in the
> sense of regimes from which light can't escape to
> infinity.[1]

The emphasis is mine. I have always admired Stephen
Hawking for one thing above all else — his principles.
When he finds that he has been wrong about something,
no matter how heavily he has invested in it, he stands on
the city hall steps and announces his error. In this case,
let us be clear about what this means. What Dr Hawking
declares in this paper is that event horizons do not exist,
and if there are no event horizons, there are no black holes.
Period.

In just a few words, he recants his entire career. Not
since Edwin Hubble has there been a demonstration of
such lofty integrity in science. And like Dr Hubble, Dr
Hawking himself trashes the very thing that brought him
his fame and his glory in the first place. Respect, ladies and
gentlemen. If only there were more like him.

But that's not the issue here. The crucial point, about
which this whole chapter and indeed my entire thesis
turns, is the role played in Dr Hawking's international
success by public awareness of the above list of achievements. It is to all intents and purposes non-existent. The
overwhelming majority of Hawking fans would be shocked
and bewildered if they were to read my list. They adore

---

1 S.W. Hawking, "Information Preservation and Weather Forecasting for
black holes" (date TK) doi: arxiv: 1401.5761.

Stephen Hawking and regard him as a superior human being, before whom they supplicate themselves in a quest for enlightenment. Yet they neither know nor understand nor care even what his philosophy is.

They just believe.

Whenever a theory appears to you as the only possible one, take this as a sign that you have neither understood the theory nor the problem which it was intended to solve.

KARL POPPER

Human behaviour is driven or at least enhanced by the same set of psycho-chemical "fight-or-flight" secretions that flow in the blood of Vervet monkeys and Steppe wolves; whether we are contentedly accepting or angrily aggressive is underpinned by biochemistry, and it is those chemicals that to a large extent define our personalities. The same sort of subconscious stimulus that fires up our defence of nest and offspring does duty in our obsessive protection of the opinions stamping identities onto our psyches. The belief instinct is as strong as any other governing the organisation of individuals in society.

9

THE $64,000 QUESTION

What the heck can we do about it?

IN THE DUST DEVIL dance of that classic contemporary western called *No Country for Old Men*, an implacable drug-mob assassin named Anton Chigurh catches up with his prey in a hotel room just a stone's throw from the Rio Grande. The chips are down. Chigurh is a chilling psychopath about to deliver the *coup de grâce* to the battle weary fugitive Carson Wells. Their conversation is one of the most quotable quotes in the history of cinema.

> **Anton Chigurh:** And you know what's going to happen now. You should admit your situation. There would be more dignity in it.
> **Carson Wells:** You go to hell.
> **Anton Chigurh:** *(chuckles)*: Alright. Let me ask you something. If the rule you followed brought you to this, of what use was the rule?

The metaphor may be a bit strong, but the message is right on the money. Unlike my previous books, this one is not going to conclude with my saying, "*There. That's what's wrong*", and without further ado, taking my hat and coat to go home for tea. In this book, I'm saying that *everything* is wrong, and unless I can suggest a way out, I shall no doubt be hung forthwith from the yardarm. That is neither my future vision nor the preferred conclusion for my long-suffering self, so believe me, it is not the way I'm going bid you farewell here.

As far as I know, this work charts new territory. It is both novel and tentative; the philosophy I'm putting forward here came from not much more than life skills I picked up at the rock face of space science. I mention this because scientific pragmatism is not by any stretch of the imagination in its ultimate, useable form. If it has any merit at all, then there is going to be a great deal of debate around these issues, and my colleagues in the halls of academia — following the true spirit of the scientific method — will no doubt panel-beat it into shape. That is my wish and my hope, at any rate.

The good news is that my philosophy has no pretensions of grandeur. Nearly all of it has come to me by means of dialogue, in natural, conversational English. I did not need mathematics — *at all* — to understand these things, nor do I need even the tiniest bit of mathematics to express them. This chatty sort of approach puzzles earnest scholars, and I am often greeted by "are you *serious*? Really?"

Yes I am, deadly serious. Belief is a common resident, despite the fact that less than one hundredth of one percent of the human population of Mother Earth is adept at metamathematics. There is nothing elitist or exclusive about scientific pragmatism.

The final leg of our journey with *Socks* is going to involve something terrible. The cleansing process involves the letting of blood. I am speaking figuratively of course, but that makes it no less daunting. We need to let go of our deepest beliefs. For some unspecified period of realignment, I'm asking Christians to put their Bibles aside; Muslims to cleave themselves from Muhammed; cosmologists to cancel their Big Bang subscriptions; and capitalists to look past the dollar. In a strange kind of way, I'm expecting us all to commit suicide. No, not the Jim Jones brand of theological mass murder, but a frightening prospect nonetheless. We are defined by our beliefs, so giving them up means losing the comfort of an identity that we have loved for so long. We will experience discomfort; there's no doubt about that. It's called cold turkey.

My hope by now is that my reader will have accepted that our search for truth is best approached by objectivity. This is fundamental; objectivity can be attained only if we somehow set aside our natural and compelling tendency to look at the world with feeling. And here it is that I am walking barefoot over broken glass and rusty fish hooks. Belief is *such* an emotional thing.

I am a believer as much as anyone, and my world view is undoubtedly coloured by my own prejudice. What I am going to suggest in this concluding chapter is a systematic approach by which we can more closely align our stubborn mindset with objective truth. I'm not offering an alternative model. I'm not selling an explanation of the universe. What I'm asking everyone, especially my brethren in science, is to urgently review the *method* they employ. If we can but reduce the contamination inherent in method, we will automatically be more clearly exposed to objective truth. We need to wipe some mud off the foundations before we build our castles of light.

In a nutshell, *Socks* does not seek to correct existing belief and remove prejudice from the table of discussion; that appears impracticable in any event. The basic premise underpinning scientific pragmatism is simply this: From here on in, when we build our personal models of existence, we must at all costs construct the foundation from objective truth, or as close to objective truth as we can possibly get in practice. If the first line of bricks is subjective, imagined, metaphysical, occult, superstitious, or purely hypothetical, we are lost before we start. If we keep that ethic in our mind's eye as we build our hypo-stacks, we will be putting our personal spin on a central axis reasonably aligned with the world about us. If we take our ideas and toss them out of the window, and they immediately fall to Earth, then they have mass. For the umpteenth time, I say this: The only way to test a theory is against external, common reality.

There are some principles given in this work governing the acquisition and arrangement of knowledge that I think are fairly well established and supported by substantial empirical experience. The first order of business is to grasp the basics: We all have belief; our opinions are conspicuously tainted by it. Furthermore, belief is something we like about ourselves, so much so that it forms a powerful reinforcement of our self-esteem. We enjoy the experience and will not give it up lightly. In fact, most of us would fight to keep our beliefs with as much zeal as we defend our homes.

The real issue that challenges our progress as a species is not simply a matter of identifying the effect of belief on our ability to advance, or indeed even summarizing the challenges associated with belief, as I have done in this book. Nor is it devising a solution for the havoc that belief wreaks in our lives, as I am trying to do in this concluding chapter. Many fine scholars and dedicated objectivists that came before me have done all that, and published their results for our scrutiny.

No more beating about the bush; here is the crux of the matter. The issue is far more vexing than merely exposing the negativity that belief brings to the table; the problem that seems to guarantee our continuing subjugation by irrational convictions is our apparent inability to take whatever truths we may discover and apply those solutions to our own beliefs. We slash and burn with glee at the beliefs of others, all the while clinging like babies to our own. That's the problem. We make of ourselves the glittering exception, and right there we fail.

This is clearly the most challenging chapter in my book. We can easily see the harmful effects of subjective preconception, and quite understand that true knowledge needs to be acquired free of belief's ubiquitous filter. Yet we hang on to our beliefs like life itself. Here I note a distinct parallel with drug addiction. Despite the fact that the addict knows full well at an intellectual level that his habit is terribly bad for him and leads him into darkness, his judgement has become infected by the experience. He clings to it so stubbornly that one might be forgiven for thinking he is quite mad. Addiction is nothing more than chemically supported belief.

The fact of the matter is quite simply that some people are going to get it and some are not, no matter how deft my explanation. The trend I have recognised in human behaviour regarding the effects of belief on the reinforcement of opinions makes no exception for my benefit. There will be readers who take in what I've said with great sincerity, express their awe at the revolution it has brought to their world view, and then with even greater conviction colour it so richly with the oils of their own faith that my intended meaning is quite lost on them going forward. That's the harsh reality of belief, and I shall simply have to take it on the chin.

The $64,000 question therefore starts with the preface that the believer really *wants* to believe as he does and act out on those beliefs in his life. No matter that his reasoning in support really sucks, how can we expect him to intellectualise his way out of it?

The cumulative effect of belief on the human psyche results in a personal mental colour that we call our *mindset*. It's where we *want* to be. I was at supper with friends last night and the patriarch of the family said something that caught my wandering mind: He said that his beliefs change daily, because every day he learns something new. By accepting that in the bigger picture we are predominantly ignorant, we open ourselves to novel, previously incomprehensible information every day. It should be obvious that *any* assumption we make is arbitrarily and artificially ordained. But the question that immediately begs an answer is this: Do our *beliefs* change with each passing day? I'm afraid they do not.

In a perfect world, our opinions should always and continuously be open to review. Belief is not like this. It does not sincerely encourage review of itself. Belief is utterly self-satisfied and resistant to change. The nature of the beast is deceiving; whilst we may to a large degree be open to new information, the fact remains that our mindset censors, filters, and manipulates incoming data to suit itself. Belief loves its life of privilege. We spend an inordinately large slice of our mental rumination trying to predict what criticisms of our belief might come our way, and what sort of defence we can organise against them. Belief, then, stands resolutely in denial of our ignorance.

I risk becoming repetitive, but I must; the cleansing process of the human mind prior to proceeding with scientific enquiry should (at the outset at least) take no cognisance of what is right or wrong when put up against some imagined absolute truth. That would be a very costly diversion. Our task is no more than this: Recognise the beliefs filtering our thoughts, and quarantine them. We must learn to do science independently of any model, and that, my friends, is far more difficult than one might imagine.

We should, in science and in philosophy, abandon a belief stratum not because it is wrong, but simply *because it is a belief*. The passion with which people hold a belief is not related to what it actually is that they believe in; no matter the object of their faith, they believe in that thing because they *want* to believe in it. Period. It is precisely because of that impenetrable zeal that beliefs are impervious to reason. My pragmatism dictates that I would be patently foolish to recommend that we rationalise our way out of belief; what we need to do instead is simply put our faith on ice, and embrace scientific scepticism.

It is clear to me that no matter how reasonable I try to be, I will always be biased. Bias is not the consequence of reason; it is the weight given to our opinions by belief. Belief is not reasonable, and does not come about because of rational discourse. It is a manifestation of our own assertion that we understand things better *a priori* (because of some privileged insight on our part) than those who have a different understanding. I have yet to find someone who genuinely declares that his own belief is less reasonable and more poorly thought out than the next man's; indeed, most would in their mind's eye tend to use the term "objective truth" rather than "belief" when describing their own opinions.

The energy with which we cling to our own beliefs is incredible, even among those who claim to have no belief. Furthermore, one's own belief is almost always taken to be more reasonable and less inherently "mere belief" than the arguments presented against our position. It follows from this that their holding a different opinion or presenting an alternative understanding means that those of different persuasion *oppose* us. This is key: My belief is *better* than your belief, quite irrespective of what those beliefs might be, and therefore it becomes a manifestation of territorial warfare — the battle for high ground and tacit confirmation of sought-after superiority of self. Dialogue becomes diatribe; calm reason sharpens its claws for a fight. Belief is the cloak worn by egotism.

In every case, our approach to a proposal should be sceptical. If we simply accept an assertion, it is a sure sign

that we form what I call a *belief-synapse*[1], and it is readily
absorbed into our personal dogma. To make the sceptical
approach effective in a practical sense, we should ignore
for the time being whether or not the idea under review
is true; we must simply detach it from the chain of belief.
This will no doubt seem troublesome and time-consuming,
but we must endeavour to be almost superhuman in our
objectivity. Thus, if we hear the suggestion that elephants
became telepathically aware of Lawrence Anthony's death
(see Chapter Four), and gathered at his home and else-
where in some sort of mourning ritual, we initially reject
it. No matter how much we may like the idea, and notwithstanding the possibility that the proposal might in fact
be true, we reject it. Without malice of forethought, we
project purity into our enquiry. As closely as possible, we
demonstrate pristine scepticism at the outset.

The essence of empirical scientific pragmatism is this:
Our very first reaction on being presented with an hypothesis, quite irrespective of what it may claim, is to try to
falsify it. We shouldn't look for evidence in favour until we
have exhaustively searched for evidence against it. The vat
in which we brew our potions must, of necessity, be constructed of the stoutest scepticism. Theories that appeal to
our gut survive much more easily to become golden calves,
because they mesmerise us. Belief is an instinct, and it
rewards us with good feeling and pride. Like a siren on the

---

[1] Belief-synapse: A virtual data-passing connection between articles of
belief; an information bus that allows unrestricted flow between existing dogma and received belief. Belief-synapse allows the rapid creation or
extension of a hypo-stack.

rocks, it seduces us with irresistible beauty, and we lose our capacity to be cautiously doubtful.

Of course, it is so much easier to doubt when there is no belief-synapse present and the idea at the outset doesn't make sense to us. We would be readily sceptical were that the case. Conversely, it becomes exponentially harder to be sincerely sceptical when the incoming idea sounds attractive. That's the burden the objective scientist has to carry. No one said life would be easy!

What then is my solution to the problem? First of all, we need to inculcate an empirical mindset. This is easier said than done; so by way of introduction, please allow me to repeat a passage from the prologue to this work. I owe my late father a huge debt of gratitude for impressing upon me the value of what I would in later years call *reality physics*. He spoke to me about physics and mechanics, cause and effect, from the time that I was first able to hold memory in my mind's eye. The way he put this philosophy to me seemed so simple that it appeared to be patently naive, yet it would take me until well into my adult years before I grasped what the meanings of these idioms were.

- The truth belongs to no one.
- No hocus-pocus.
- Beware the man with a theory.
- Never negotiate with a suicide bomber.
- For every effect, there's a cause, and for every action, a reaction.

Crucially, *before* we conclude that the model is true or false, we need to reboot, clear the RAM, reset, and have a cup of tea. Assessing the effect of belief has nothing, I repeat, *nothing* to do with whether the model is true or not. Most generally, I find this: Your model may well contain significant truth, but not for the reasons you've cited. Your supporting arguments are weak, flawed, or plainly fallacious, but that neither proves nor disproves the assertion. Therefore, with respect to your theory, I must remain agnostic. I don't know that your idea is the correct answer, nor do I know that it is incorrect. The onus then reverts to you; you need to re-examine your assumptions if you wish to convince me (you may not, of course). Until such time as you succeed in overcoming my healthy scepticism, I shall be inclined to say that I *do not believe* your hypothesis.

It's worth repeating: I do not believe you, but I am not saying your assertion is wrong. I am simply not yet convinced by the evidence raised.

This principle was the whole point of my book *The Static universe*. I have no rational grounds to insist that the Big Bang model is inherently false; I do however have compelling reason to suspect that the supporting evidence is weak, flawed, or factually untenable. I have erred on the side of caution, and taken a conservative, somewhat stubborn point of view. Big Bang theory is an extraordinary hypothesis, involving great stretches of imagination, and it's going to take extraordinarily robust evidence to get me to accept that it correctly describes actual reality. This leads to several interesting implications.

Firstly, I am admittedly being reactionary and am often accused of resisting progress. If I do this often enough — and believe me, I do — I will sooner or later be called an iconoclast, simply against anything orthodox. I dispute this description. Beliefs are a dime a dozen; I typically receive by email several theoretical models or hypotheses to do with the universe in a day, and they are invariably accompanied by explicit or implicit requests for my evaluation. These include complete cosmologies and theories of everything. Here's the thing: For every ten competing cosmologies, only one at most could be properly correct. At least nine are wrong. My experience in the field has demonstrated beyond a shadow of a doubt that the overwhelming majority of cosmological theories are fatally flawed, unsupported by the cited evidence, or just flights of imagination. They must consequently be doubtful starters as realistic, compelling answers to the biggest questions we can ask.

It is unavoidable that I reject more theories than I accept; that's just the nature of the beast. In *The Virtue of Heresy*, I gave hard examples: Three great systems of science — Newtonian mechanics, quantum mechanics, and Einstein's relativity, though each is proudly successful in its own right — conflict with one another. Not even the immeasurably vast volume of analysis and profound thought by many, many brilliant people (including he whose name decorates this book) for a hundred years or more has been able to effect reconciliation. Where does that leave you and me?

Secondly, we see the application of unseemly haste in accepting theories. In *The static universe*, I demonstrated arduously (with no rebuttal that I'm aware of) that the current standard model of cosmology has a factual base so weak that one might argue that real supporting evidence is nonexistent. The original galaxian redshift pattern announced by Edwin Hubble in 1929 was soon found to have been an illusion, and the accidental discovery of a microwave background radiation fog was re-engineered quite blatantly to force a fit with the preferred model. In both cases, the evidence was anticipated and readily accepted by the eager throng well before it had been properly tested. And the model remains in force long after the supporting data have been discredited. This is how belief works.

Let's review:

- A superficially appreciated model is preferred because "it makes sense" — in other words, it finds favour with existing preconceptions.
- Subsequently, evidence is sought with the specific intention of establishing a factual base upon which to construct and reinforce the model. Note that this intention occurs *before* the model has been empirically verified.
- Fudging and sophistry are applied to data sets so that they appear to give the required answer.

In many cases, evidence is conjured out of nothing (for example, miracles). This aspect of belief is of great interest to psychologists and theologists, and has been well described in the literature.

The disparity in stringency of verification between subsequent results favouring the preferred model and those results critical of it is laughable. Opposing evidence is gone through with a fine-tooth comb, whilst data supporting the model, no matter how contrived, is embraced with the same level of unseemly haste that blessed the model in the first place.

It's a tough nut to crack. After all, we are dealing with hard-wired instinct, a fundamental *need* to believe. It is possible though to modify one's attitude. The first step I constantly apply to my own understanding is to be passively in denial. If I do not believe in the wrathful God of Abraham, then I should express my scepticism softly. Becoming assertive and evangelical about it soon transforms "*not* believe" into "*believe* not" and the difference is profound. We convert ignorance into belief. In this way, atheism is simply belief of a different hue. The reasonable point of view for someone who is not convinced that God exists is agnosticism. It is an admission and an expression of ignorance, and *that*, my friends, is nothing less than noble honesty.

There are some well-worn markers that guide me. They include:

- Proceed always from the standpoint of ignorance. The motto is "*I do not yet know.*"
- Engineering approach. Look upon every model as the proposed solution to a real-world problem. This approach at the outset rests crucially upon the clear declaration in first principles of the problem to be solved. A good example is NASA's space exploration programme.
- Become quite clear on the principles governing faith-based opinions. Do this by examining belief other than your own.

- Examine the model as a solution to problems other than your own.
- Identify and exorcise the bandwagon. This refers to ideas that are opportunistically associated, though they really have nothing to do with each other, for example, linking research on coral degradation to climate change to win political favour and funding.
- Do not entertain faint or subjective evidence — that is, avoid any part of the model that is not solidly verified. This includes claims by the model's author that it has passed stringent empirical tests. Examples are personal experiences, supernatural phenomena, miracles, religious epiphanies, arbitrary interpretations of data, and hypo-stacking.
- Explain only something that has been observed. This is crucial. We should not attempt to explain something that has only been imagined.
- Never accept tenets of theory purely on the authority or reputation of its proponents, or the esteem in which you hold them.
- Any theory or model must in principle be falsifiable, and able to be tested against reality. Tests against other theories or models or against the syntax of expression are not valid, nor are tests against prior layers in a hypo-stack.

- Testing against reality carries the critical constraint that it should be current reality; testing against historical reality or an imagined future world are impossible and therefore invalid. Gedankenexperiments prove nothing at all.
- Testing is always strictly independent of any alternative model or replacement theory.

The essence of scientific pragmatism is the engineering approach. We need to separate physics and philosophy while we're busy obtaining the principles. When the time comes to build our philosophical appreciation of the world, we should be sure that the data upon which we construct these more elaborate opinions were properly obtained; instead of letting them spring forth from an intuitive reservoir and wash over us like a tide, I'm suggesting that we create or mould our beliefs from the principles of physics (by *physics* I mean broader empirical scientific objectivism).

Here is something of vital importance to the success or otherwise of scientific pragmatism. Before we start our investigation, we need to be very clear what the problem is. If our conception of the problem is itself wrapped in belief, we are lost before we start. So the very first step we need to take on this adventure, right after we've filled the teapot, and right before we first raise a hand in anger, is to *reduce the subject of our analysis to first principles and write that down.*

To illustrate what I mean, I have devised a clinical test of scientific pragmatism which I shall briefly describe here.

We are near the end of the book, the principles regarding belief have been satisfactorily obtained, and I am thus now free to apply SP to tenets of my own belief.

Since this is the first (to my knowledge) proper clinical test of scientific pragmatism as a disinfectant of belief in science, consider what follows as a draft framework. Clearly, the way that I express myself on the subject of climate — even by the choice of quotes I lace into the social media — is an expression of belief on my part. Having identified the belief I am carrying, my next task is to quarantine it, taking no regard whatsoever of whether it is right or wrong. Then, independently of any model, I look at the data. How I interpret the data against objective criteria will determine what my opinion on the matter becomes. That's the end of the cycle. To increase my self-knowledge, I can afterwards compare my opinions before SP and after SP. It should be interesting.

Belief manifests most often as an alignment with one side or the other in polarised opinions. Agnosticism (objectivity) occupies the middle ground. No one who has read this far would have missed that in the great twenty-first-century climate debate, I am definitely on the side of the "deniers" and opposed to the "alarmists." Perfect. Let's put it onto the dissection table. SP might just as well stand for *surgical procedure*.

I must emphasise very strongly that it is not that I have an opinion on the matter that is the problem; it's that my opinion is shaped by my beliefs rather than the data. The dead giveaway is my attitude — both the zeal with which I cling to my position as well as my passionate expression of the doctrine of denial. Emotion is the surest sign of subjectivity.

The first step, as we have discussed above, is to identify the essence of the issue causing the polarity. I must avoid any hint of bias, and definitely eliminate sarcasm. My first pass at a definition of the issue produced this:

1. The Earth is becoming catastrophically warmer.
2. The warming and associated effects can be alleviated and controlled by the reduction of human carbon dioxide output.

I am now ready to proceed. I may want to sharpen my definition of the climate issue as I go along, but this is a good enough start. Throughout this process, I shall have to be on my guard against bias. It will take great discipline on my part, but habits can be learned. At all times, I must eschew the contempt with which I had previously regarded the alarmists. In fact, this is not the time to be considering specific opinions, irrespective of where they lie. The issue I am tackling is indeed a set of opinions, encapsulated in the anthropogenic global warming model, but let that be the last time I look at opinions before the end of this test. I am now ready for the hard data, viewed objectively and entirely without the filter of any hypothetical model.

That's about as much as needs to be said here. Because the example I used is a matter of science, I am going to have to draw on my training as a physicist to analyse the data, all the while strictly confining myself to the basic tools of physics and strenuously avoiding any pre-existing model or hypothesis. In other words, I shall be employing laws and avoiding conjecture. Mathematics will be confined to its role as symbolic arithmetic, useful only to obtain quantities. The data will receive intensive scrutiny, not least the means by which they were obtained. I should let the facts fall where they will. At the end of this phase of investigation, I should be able to draw a tentative conclusion, and consider it from my perspective as a scientific agnostic.

Here we are then, ready to cross the Rubicon. I shall lead from the front; as soon as I am done writing, I'll set to the task of dismantling my own beliefs, favourites first, and building a new, independent world view. It will be painful at first, I know that, but I also anticipate the thrill of liberation. Like the rest of my species, I have been kept stooped under the yoke laid upon my shoulders by the illusion of knowledge. As shocking as it may be to admit, it is a self-inflicted burden, and I alone have the means to free myself. It may seem patently counterintuitive, but I must nevertheless allow myself no latitude in reinventing subjectively ordained knowledge so that I am at the threshold of discovery, armed only with objective ignorance. It sounds a bit silly to say it like that, but I think you get what I mean.

If I happen to be unconvinced that Hawking's description of black holes is realistic, that shouldn't mean I'm opposed to him. Remember, our goal is scientific agnosticism. We should apply whatever it takes to convert our beliefs into non-belief; our zeal for a cause into calm detachment: "I know" into "I do not yet know".

This would demand great discipline on our part, and indeed, endless patience. The unseemly haste with which we pursue the intellectual and moral high ground is our downfall, and all it does is pump steroids into the fibres of our belief. The enemy in this campaign protects itself with a suit of dogma, and we need the courage to recognise it in ourselves too.

Stephen Hawking, by sheer coincidence, leads the charge. When I set out to write this book, I had no glimmer of foresight that he would himself set an example so profound in its implications that other cited case studies would pale by comparison and become almost superfluous. All his working life, Professor Hawking had steadfastly insisted that he *did* know what black holes were; shortly after his 71st birthday, he finally admitted that he did not. He cast a pall of doubt onto his defining belief, the very backbone of his personal philosophy, and for a believer, there can be nothing more courageous than that. While his followers desperately try to rescue black holes from ignominy by proposing mathematical escape clauses like "grey holes" and other such nonsense, Dr Hawking is immutable. He knows that without a horn on its forehead, a unicorn is just a horse.

He did not deny his god, nor declare it dead. He merely said, "I do not know", and that, my friends, is what philosophy is all about: Exploring our ignorance. Our certainty about black holes was an abject illusion, and by some unfathomable quirk of fate, it was Hawking himself who popped the bubble. That he should have waited until this book was practically completed — and it is unlikely that he would at that time ever have heard of it — is an intriguing nuance of careless fortune. But he did provide me with an unexpectedly pleasing way to bring my work to a close.

At the end of the day, if I'm correct in my thesis, we will begin to comprehend that our armour did not shield us from harm so much as it debarred us from comprehending the truth.

We now have eight, going on nine chapters behind our backs, and I should hope that we have managed to get the basics down pat. With commendable obedience, we have examined belief by very strictly excluding our own from the study. We have looked at a wide variety of manifestations of faith-based bias, and I'm satisfied that we have been sufficiently thorough. With that part of our journey complete, we now face the ultimate test: applying the rules we have obtained to ourselves and to our most precious personal creeds. We're done talking; now we walk the walk.

There, I've said it.

That which can be asserted
without evidence, can be
dismissed without evidence.

CHRISTOPHER HITCHENS

 sn't it strange when you tell people that you like cats that they invariably assume you don't like dogs? That liking tea automatically gets taken to mean a dislike of coffee? That being gay somehow implies you're anti-straight? That taking conventional medicine makes one opposed to herbal remedies? I call this the cat-and-dog rule—the baseless assumption of polarity in opinions. It stems from the misconception that polarity is caused by prejudice.

BUZZ CLIPS

Sex, drugs, and rock'n roll

WITH *SOCKS* BEHIND US now, there remains only one more thing to be done, and we can all take a well-earned break. You've heard me going on like a stuck record about reducing things to first principles. Well, here they are for *Socks*. I read through the book with the singular purpose of spotlighting phrases and paragraphs that I think distil the essence of our message to the world. Glance through them. It should be easy reading by now, and it will help to consolidate the philosophy that needs to be shared if it is to do any good at all. Here goes.

> Scientists are above all human beings, with all the foibles and limitations that their species generally expresses. Scientists are neither superhuman nor divine-

ly privileged. Scientists, let me tell you right now, are simply plodding bricklayers in the wall of knowledge.

We strut our stuff amongst the biological diversity of our lonely blue planet as it speeds towards an unseen destiny, proclaiming ourselves advanced merely because we have the faculty of abstract thought — the singular privilege of being able to think about thought, to juggle between the senses and a self-centred theory of mind, and to furiously engage in sharing our imaginations with anyone who dares to listen.

It would appear that disagreeing with instinct is a dichotomy peculiar to the human species; other animals, though as capable as we are of making choices in the moment, are not as far as I can tell perplexed and misled by such an elaborate belief in the sanctity of their own opinions.

The kings of knowledge are all-powerful in the realm they administer, and it has surely corrupted them. Like despots anywhere, they should (figuratively speaking, of course) be put to the sword, and let the next king ascend to start the whole caboodle all over again.

It is my contention that there is a viable remedy for our ills, but in order to consider my proposal we are going to have to suspend, temporarily at least, that most precious and jealously guarded of all our possessions — our beliefs.

I do not question Islam because I am a Christian; I do not critique Christianity because I am a Jew; I do not deny Mayan doomsday ideas because they conflict with my belief in Nostradamus; I do not challenge Greenpeace because I am a member of the National Rifle Association; and I do not attack the 9/11 conspiracy theories because I am a Republican. In every case, I assess those belief systems using the objective scientific method, and in every case they are found wanting. And I remain in all cases an agnostic.

In the unforgiving post-graduate world where I was expected to apply my knowledge usefully to the satisfaction of my benefactors, I slowly came to realise that education was a form of classical conditioning in the Pavlovian mode; we were its dogs, and both the tricks we were to perform and the rewards we would consequently receive were made abundantly clear to us.

The stars are real things, every one of them far bigger than our Earth, and unimaginably hotter. They have a vast range of physical properties not nearly obvious to the naked eye, and in our ignorance we create a Christmas tree up there in the heavens.

The real insidiousness of this imaginative method of describing actuality is that it's a slippery slope. It commences by addressing a cosmic mystery with nothing more than a little white lie, and all too soon it escalates into a fully fledged multitiered belief paradigm, replete with mesmerising black holes, dark energies, and Noah's arks.

We test the principles of democracy against beliefs most commonly held in the tribe; we validate the tenets of science against reality itself. No matter what we believe about gravitation, quite irrespective of the words we use in describing it, and taking no account at all of what we would like gravitation to be, we can test it, all of us, by jumping off the garden shed. Gravitation is impartial and pays no heed to our philosophical persuasion. We hit the ground equally, and that's what we urgently need to take note of before we get lost in a maze of dreams.

Isn't it strange that when you tell people that you like cats that they invariably assume you don't like dogs? That liking tea automatically gets taken to mean a dislike of coffee? That being gay somehow implies you're anti-straight? That taking conventional medicine makes one opposed to herbal remedies? I call this the cat-and-dog rule — the baseless assumption of polarity in opinions. It stems from the misconception that polarity is caused by prejudice.

No matter what my personal beliefs may or may not be, I have always maintained that religion has no function in science. Faith in God has its own place, and its own way of exploring its knowledge base. Indeed, I have no problem with religionists using science as an element in their internal debates — provided of course that they do not twist the science to fit their argument. But the reverse is unacceptable to me. Science is secular and should remain independent of any and all theological models.

We are not going to evolve into noble creatures; we are going to evolve into a tribe aligned with our chemical destiny. The crocodile is not going to evolve into a vegetarian, or at least, not because it has an ethical objection to killing wildebeests.

Science progresses by exploring the unknown, finding the unexpected, and being challenged by sceptics. The quest for knowledge is a search for things we don't already know. It is, when all is said and done, an exploration of our ignorance.

One of the most compelling aspects of astronomy for me is in getting to know that the stars don't care. In the big scheme, I am nearly nothing; so close to infinitely trivial as makes no difference. I can try to be a big fish in a small pond and bask in the applause, but I should know that the stars are not going to blink. They have much more important things to attend to, and that's good to know.

Scientists wanted to play God, and by Jiminy, they've done it. The Higgs boson is not the last time they'll refer to one of their solutions as being related to a superbeing with whom they have ostensibly engineered a cosy line of communication.

It is a principle of democratic governance that the effectiveness of the process depends critically upon the vibrancy of the opposition. If in parliament there is no effective opposition, then government tends towards virtual dictatorship, no matter that members were democratically elected in the first place. There is no doubt that science is governed. There are rules, and the rules are enforced.

Remove the constraint of external reality and you invite into the psyche a delusional condition where the mathematician consciously or unconsciously becomes "master of the universe." All the good work of abstract mathematics is seriously undermined by the psychological instability it induces.

That is not to say that metamathematicians are all raving lunatics — some are, definitely, but many are not. They still walk their dogs, pay their parking tickets, and remember to get dressed in the morning. And sometimes, rarely though, even talk intelligibly. It is in their contention that external reality is as they define it that they come dangerously close to fitting clinical description of insanity.

Many a true word is said in jest. Here is the mantra for our meditation: *In the song of the sky, we make out a 3D rendition of our personal God.* An instinctive preset in our cognitive mechanisms means that we can always find signal where there is actually just noise.

Faith provides a preferred explanation. Thus it is that Christians ascribe their recovery to faith in Jesus, Hindus to karma, Buddhists to right living, atheists to themselves, and Muslims to the grace of Islam. One's belief system determines a particular, exclusive causal dynamic for conditions that in actuality strike anyone without prejudice, regardless of the badge their point of view hides behind.

To the scientific mind, belief systems are crazy; they revolve around paranormal or extra-normal phenomena. But they also have an internal justification mechanism. On their own terms, they are legitimate, and tend to consider their doctrines to be an expression of profound wisdom. The "word of God" is a rubber stamp for anything.

If we hold the opinion that the Sun is the nucleus of the Solar System because we interpret a passage in the Bible that way, it is belief; if on the other hand we maintain the very same opinion as a result of geometrical measurement and observation, it is knowledge. If we accept and embrace the validity of general relativity theory simply because we think Albert Einstein is awesome, we express belief; if our support of the model comes from stringent empirical testing, it is knowledge.

It thus became clear that I would not get to the objective science of belief unless I could somehow extract myself from the vortex. Like it or not, I had to accept the stark reality: In the search for objective truth, all belief is a negative filter — all of it, most especially my own. For the scientist, there can be no exceptions to this.

People who claim to be able to free themselves from gravity's eternal clutch and float up into the sky, and those who assure us they can time-travel and manipulate past and future remotely from the present moment, are nuts. Sorry. They are. Put another way, we could say they've been smoking their socks. They've simply lost their grasp on the real world's reference frame.

The double-malted philosopher-mathematician Bertrand Russell could in the midst of all his turbulent thought and convoluted conceptualising still manage to give us some gems of brevity. "Sin is geographical", he said once, and it quite took my breath away.

It was a terrifying thought, especially for poor Copernicus, a man of the cloth who was expected to toe the party line. He wrote his vision into his watershed book *On the Revolutions of Heavenly Spheres* and hid the manuscript in a box under his bed for more than thirty years.

The power of ownership — whether of fixed property or intellectual assets — shows up in no uncertain terms when it is under threat. Belief is treated no differently from territory or progeny by the owner, and he will defend it vigorously.

I want to emphasise that our study seeks to address belief in a secular way, and delineate its role in secular matters particularly. For a number of reasons, I wish by all means to avoid reducing this investigation to an argument about religion. At the same time, it is simply not scholarly to leave religion out of contention as a source of case studies.

Belief belongs in religion; there, it enjoys a welcoming, compatible environment in which to flourish. It is where we can find prime examples to illustrate the driving principles. Religionists are charmingly open about their propensity for belief, and seem proud of it. Scientists are quite the opposite.

At a fundamental level, in their reflection of first principles, beliefs found in atheism, Islam, cosmology, or Christianity are in no essential aspect different from one another. They differ only in the way they express detail; at their roots, they are astonishingly similar. And that, my friends, is what makes my mission so difficult to achieve.

Belief is a powerful agency. Belief shapes our thinking and guides our behaviour to such an extent that we often become blind to the chicanery of snake oil charlatans. We sometimes let our adulation turn us into factories blithely manufacturing imaginary evidence to support premises founded upon nothing more than slick illusion.

Devotees who are intoxicated by belief will invariably fabricate evidence in support of their beliefs. More alarming still, they appear to have no qualms about subjectively bending the truth. What they wish to be true blurs what is actually true, so the well-meaning witness appears to have no moral compunction at all.

It seems as if we are owned by our belief system, and that a great deal of time and effort is spent defending it. The crucial point is that belief precedes the logic used to validate it.

Scepticism has shifted the hierarchy. From being an entertaining but minor inflection on the methodology of science, it has in my view emerged as the only thing that can save our objective knowledge base from implosion. Without it we are lost, with no more control and no fewer thrills than a super-duper roller-coaster ride.

There is nothing in my experience that's more damning of useable truth in scientific endeavour than unseemly haste. The unchecked speed with which the canon grows condemns us to unflinchingly pursue doctrine by indoctrination.

The doctrine that emerges from the philosophy of iconic religious figures is always the outcome of organising the church; the doctrine is a political manifest, not a theological one. Religion is the political expression of theology.

Fairies are not put forward as real creatures by any but a very small band of naive dreamers, so serious discussion and dedicated thought time are not warranted. The matter of religion and the God hypothesis is quite different though, and deserves to be studied, if for no other reason than that it is a widely held sociological trend.

Thus we have the conversion of a theological model into a political movement, with all that the term implies. Part of that implication is the method employed to ensure the fertility of their doctrine in the minds of generations to come. Without exception, religious methodology centrally involves indoctrination. The main business of a cult is indoctrination. It is the most important thing they do.

Every hypothesis should be greeted with scepticism. I mean this: every single one, no exceptions. We find merit with new ground not because it matches the data but for no better reason than that it harmonises with our preconceptions.

By far most of the New Testament scholars are Christians. Many are tenured in Christian Bible colleges. They are subjectively committed a priori to a belief in the standard doctrinal inferences of the scriptures they are studying. They are not trying to falsify the model. Indeed, quite the contrary. Their investigation is intent on no more than fine-tuning their preconceptions.

Belief is a conviction held independently of rational discourse. In fact, belief or faith is held by a broad cross-section of believers to be superior to intellectual analysis and in their minds dominates it. What is not generally recognised is that belief is not the exclusive province of religion; far from it. In scientific parlance, beliefs are called *axioms*.

The reason that standard models become as entrenched and zealously defended as they have been is sociological, and has almost nothing to do with physics or chemistry. Scientists, for all their bravado about objectivity, are after all as human as you or I, and demonstrate just the same passion for the canonisation of their opinions as politicians and religionists do.

Paradigm shifts have been dreadfully slow in coming about. It's not that the science indicating change was weak; it's simply that the rulers of society, as in Church and Crown, have such an exaggerated aversion to being shown wrong. Politicians and clergy, it seems to me, would in many cases rather die than admit they were fundamentally incorrect in their assumptions, and when they reach out to take ownership of a scientific theory, heaven help us.

It is clear that belief is an instinctual compulsion, a primordial need for comfort, security against the unknown. Whatever form it may take, we all have it, without exception as far as I can tell.

Belief suppresses our faculty for intelligent discrimination, and can powerfully influence our opinions. It eliminates scepticism about the articles of one's faith.

There is one way — and one way only — to test a theory, and that's against reality.

It is my aim, therefore, to simply provide a method whereby one can build a new vision. We want to be sceptical, yes, but it should be pragmatic scepticism.

We might spend valuable years and a great deal of anguish debating whether Bayesian or Monte Carlo analysis returns the best picture of the dawn of creation in the haze of the cosmic microwave background radiation, or sweat endless hours of bloody calculus over the Hubble constant's projected rate of universal expansion, when at the end of the day all those esoteric constructs become completely irrelevant if the foundations of the standard model of cosmology are invalidated. We would be arguing about smoke and mirrors.

The dead giveaway is research that declares the conclusion before it even starts to gather data.

The principles that guide us are as follows: We tend to believe because we are predisposed to do so. It is a manifestation of bias. It is crucial that we bear in mind always that all belief is counterproductive to science, no matter how dearly we love it; our immediate task, therefore, is to identify and nullify the belief filter on our investigative spectacles. We need to allow a natural, uncontrived scepticism to clear the crime scene of emotion. We have a job of work to do here.

Our individual contributions are to the species, not to ourselves. We make contributions to the future like bytes make up a data stream. We live for the briefest of moments, and then we die, leaving behind a vague mark, like an exposed foothold that was not as clear before we kicked some dirt away. Each byte stands upon the head of the one before, and gives a leg-up to the one that follows. What remains at the end is not the quantum; it is the big picture to which the quantum adds a flash of colour that lives on. At some higher level that frame is so big, so all-encompassing that it lives forever. And that, I suppose, is the meaning of life.

My question to the world then is this: How come, given the great uncertainty in the information we use to make decisions on these matters, we nevertheless still take sides and believe with gritted teeth one side or the other? Where does the power of that belief come from?

Belief invariably snaps into place when one is exposed to propaganda that disseminates the idea, provided of course that the idea being put forward harmonises with one's predisposition.

One of the most annoying aspects of belief-driven behaviour is the need to proselytise. We develop a belief, become proud of it and what it says about us, and then set about projecting this garnished self-image upon the hapless folk who fall into the sweep of our radar.

It's all too easy for us to become a monkey on the back of organised religion, but that would be missing the point rather badly. Religion, by my rustic definition, is a philosophical framework in which one can respectably claim the absurd. In my view, that gives it a charming honesty that overshadows the inherent irrationality of proclaiming knowledge of a realm governed by terrifyingly omnipotent, largely grumpy deities.

We are stimulated by the idea that we have the vision to see past the veil of stupidity that smothers global opinions other than our own, and consequently claim for ourselves the moral victory of truth.

The implication is that without the requisite fluency and understanding of mathematics, one is debarred from a realistic conception of the world about us. It is shocking that these people, whose sole qualification for their position of power is advanced knowledge of an arcane, esoteric symbolic language that few in the world can understand, elevate themselves to the podium of all science. They are self-appointed, self-regulating high priests, immune to external challenge.

To me, the notion of mathematical exclusivity is utterly absurd. It locks science into a modus that protects the fundamentals from independent investigators, no matter how deep their non-mathematical knowledge may be. In effect, reality is not defined by mathematics per se, but by our ability with the language. Reality in the scheme becomes truly user-defined and observer-dependent.

I have spoken to cult members who can readily recognise the bondage of members of other cults, but are quite incapable of recognising or admitting their own. The way that belief changes one's mode of thinking, and to what degree it does so, is an enquiry being visited in this book.

Here's the thing—belief doesn't wander around aimlessly, nor do we carriers of the germ all quietly retreat to mull over our beliefs in solitude for the rest of our days. Belief tends to organise itself, inside and out.

Gangs are theatres of debauchery. They set up social islands wherein base urges are legitimate and encouraged as a sign of membership and rank within the group. In other words, they allow instincts to rule behaviour to the detriment of civilised constraint. It is an expression of protest and defiance that exaggerates the level of aggression required by instinct.

In gangs, the pleasure-taking is general to the membership, whereas in cults and sects, members are subverted more to the dark pleasures of their leaders. Polygamy and sexual control are examples of how base instincts are expressed in cults.

One of the identifying markers put forward by Dr Sieghart is that cults form closed, totalitarian societies. Not all do, but it certainly applies to the majority of cults, enough to make it a strong pointer anyway. Let's see if it fits a scientific group. The operators of the Large Hadron Collider, famous for their alleged "discovery" of the fabled Higgs boson, fit the bill rather nicely.

We are made to cower, almost literally, before these dominant authorities, as much in awe of their elevation in the hierarchy as we are fearful of their wrath. Then, in a *coup de grâce*, the whole thing is wrapped in a blanket of consensus and fraternal bonding, and voila! A cult is born.

Conspiracy theories expose the Achilles' heel of the scientific method. Belief skews our priorities and obviously hog-ties our objective scepticism. The con-

spiracy theorist can say just about anything, no matter
how outlandish, and it will be swallowed hook, line,
and sinker — all it needs to do is make government
look sufficiently sinister.

So hungry are latent conspiracists for a conspiratorial cause to immerse themselves, in that they will
take up the cudgel for almost anything imaginable.
It seems to depend largely on how well presented
the propaganda is, in other words, on the skill of spin
doctors.

As we have seen time and again, belief is an immodest precursor to the contriving of supporting evidence,
no matter what. Zealous conspiracists will find conspiracy where more sober analysts would find the
suggestion quite ludicrous.

No, it is not a sinister, political conspiracy; it is simply
economics, and the currency is the dollar, plus, more
significantly, exposure of individuals to the diabolical
possibility that after so much effort, they might just
have been wrong.

The technical excellence of optical instruments was
advancing in leaps and bounds, driven not by greed
or territorial ambition, but by our innate exploratory drive. So it was that our awe increased, and with
it, our reverence for the new elders of the faith — scientists that pushed the frontiers of knowledge by
dragging them ever outwards with an engine called

imagination. Humankind's adulation was reaching the threshold of fan hysteria.

Before long, theorists start to believe that what they imagine is actually real, and that the novel products of their conjecture may legitimately be termed "discoveries". In more arcane realms of science, this sort of delusion is rampant, and syncopated thoughts are called discoveries without embarrassment or shame.

They are talking as if they have studied an event on an actual neutron star, and that it increases our understanding of these mysteriously fascinating cosmological objects. As an astrophysicist intensely interested in neutron stars and with privileged access to the literature surrounding them, I know that the assertion being put forward by the authors of the quoted study is patently false, and it tweaks the word discovery in a terribly misleading way.

Evidence of faith is yet more faith. I cannot say with certainty that black holes do not exist, any more than I could legitimately assert without any doubt whatsoever that God does not exist. Both would be physically impossible in terms of my grasp of physics, but then again, I'm still engaged in a life-long struggle to properly explain what I see and experience directly, stuff that I can in principle measure and put under my microscope. I see no useful purpose in incorporating into my understanding those flimsy ghosts of human superstition.

My rule of thumb is that patently irrational things are excluded from the body of knowledge I carry with me; my library of opinions should reflect those things that I am reasonably certain of, and which I can confidently build into my understanding of the cosmos. I become certain not from the degree of comfort that I derive from my beliefs, but from rational, testable evidence emanating from objective enquiry. Clearly, the evidence I am speaking of should not have come from filtering experimental or observational data through the sieve of a preferred model.

I suppose, in the cold light of day, we'll eventually come to realise that black holes (and Dark Matter, dark energy), like conspiracy theories and indeed religion, are just shadows in the minds of people inclined to think like that.

My later contemplations of these things would show that in our particular species there is an alarming extension to the manic defence of territory. We take the same stance with ideas. *"Beware the man with a theory,"* my late father advised me, and how wise he was. Homo sapiens will bleed to stagnation rather than surrender its beliefs.

Whatever we propose in our idealistic quest for utopia, it should not sail in the teeth of our design paradigm. We have cellular imperatives that will triumph in the end no matter what bright ideas we come up with.

The coldness and unreachable isolation of minds behind suicide-bomb terrorism, and the completely impersonal mass murders at schools, temples, and places of entertainment are frightening; these events are hideous badges on the cloaks of modern man.

The Arab Springs have been a tearful but profound lesson in sociology. The various uprisings have lost their noble veneer, baring their vampire teeth in rich streams of core human behaviour so convoluted that I find myself wheel-spinning in my attempt to gain traction upon the science of it.

There is a gaping disparity between the intellectually expressed, theoretical will of people and the actual reality demonstrated by their tribal behaviour. Termites don't want to be free of an absolute queen. Lions are quite happy with having alpha males. The immense strength of a monitor lizard cannot withstand the collective will of army ants. Humans want to be led. Anarchy will always fail as a social system because of this.

The blaring trumpets of civil liberty may for a while drown out the quieter song of territorially secure anthropoids, but they are ultimately brought to humiliating silence by the irresistible tide of instinctive social behaviour. History, ancient and modern, past and present, bears sullen witness to the subjective brittleness of ideals when faced by the snarling adrenalin of a parent protecting its young.

We behave territorially because our instinct tells us to. The agreements and treaties and statements of intent that we so earnestly sign with one another have no more effect on our ultimate destiny than the rooster's habitual crowing has on the Sun.

People are social creatures. It's a wired-in imperative, no less influential than it is in ants, monkeys, weaver birds, sardines, bees, and elephants. Locked into our cells is a design template that constrains us as a species and is the central lynchpin that allows us to procreate and continue the mystifying relay race called life.

We represent a synthesis between two distinct pressures on the way we interact with the environment. The polarity at play in human behaviour is a dynamic represented at one extreme by instinct and at the other by belief; in between lies a narrow buffer called free will. One is a code inherited at birth and the other is a reaction to environmental stimuli in real time.

Human behaviour is driven or at least enhanced by the same set of psychochemical fight-or-flight secretions that flow in the blood of Vervet monkeys and Steppe wolves; whether we are contentedly accepting or angrily aggressive is underpinned by biochemistry, and it is those chemicals that to a large extent define our personalities. The same sort of subconscious stimulus that fires up our defence of nest and offspring does duty in our obsessive protection of the opinions stamping identities onto our psyches. The belief instinct is as strong as any other governing the organisation of individuals in society.

The intelligent being does not make the best choices based upon independent, objective analysis. It goes always with the whims of the subjective self, irrespective of how ill-considered they might be. So, the first thing we can say about intelligence is that it is not very clever.

We should not neglect the value we ascribe to our own beliefs. How many times have we heard someone say, "I am Roman Catholic (or Republican or Greenpeace or Wiccan, whatever) and proud of it." Why should we be proud? Does our opinion on an element of reality raise us above the rabble?

It is difficult to be logical about the importance of our own instincts. Let's face it, they were not rationally obtained, nor were they a matter of choice. At no stage did we check little boxes in the prenatal set-up programme to design our visceral selves. Our instincts are intrinsically part of our greater being, that superego that owns our conscious identity.

Philosophical and religious arguments aside, what is our purpose as individuals? Why are we alive, and what is it that our design paradigm is so determined for us to achieve individually that it gives us almost irresistibly enticing chemical instructions to stay alive as long as we possibly can, and to copulate more enthusiastically and with less regard to cost than just about anything else we do? It must be for propagation of the species. Nothing else makes sense.

War is not inhuman. It is the most human, the most archetypal of all our varied flavours of social expression. Territorial conflict defines us as a species. This may seem like a profoundly cynical view to you, but one has to be realistic. We are machines of conflict, hard-wired to compete at all costs.

No more beating about the bush; this is the crux of the matter. The issue is far more vexing than merely exposing the negativity that belief brings to the table; the problem that seems to guarantee our continuing subjugation by irrational convictions is our apparent inability to take whatever truths we may discover and apply those solutions to our own beliefs.

Belief is utterly self-satisfied and strongly resists change. The nature of the animal is deceiving; whilst we may to a large degree be open to new information, the fact remains that our mindset censors, filters, and manipulates incoming data to suit itself. Belief loves its life of privilege.

The cleansing process of the human mind prior to proceeding with scientific enquiry should (at the outset at least) take no cognisance of what is right or wrong when put up against some imagined absolute truth. That would be a very costly diversion. Our task

is no more than this: Recognise the beliefs filtering
our thoughts, and quarantine them. We must learn
to do science independently of any model, and that,
my friends, is far more difficult than one might readily comprehend.

It is clear to me that no matter how reasonable I try
to be, I will always be biased. Bias is not the consequence of reason; it is the weight given to our opinions
by belief. Belief is not reasonable, and does not come
about because of rational discourse. It is a manifestation of our own assertion that we understand things
better a priori (because of some privileged insight
on our part) than those who have a different understanding.

The essence of empirical scientific pragmatism is
this: Our very first reaction on being presented with
a hypothesis, quite irrespective of what it may claim,
is to try to falsify it. We shouldn't look for evidence
in favour until we have exhaustively searched for evidence against it.

I have no rational grounds to insist that the Big Bang
model is inherently false; I do however have compelling reason to believe that the supporting evidence is
weak, flawed, or factually untenable.

The first step I constantly apply to my own understanding is to be passively in denial. If I do not believe
in the wrathful God of Abraham, then I should

express my scepticism softly. Becoming assertive and evangelical about it soon transforms "not believe" into "believe not" and the difference is profound.

The essence of scientific pragmatism is the engineering approach. We need to separate physics and philosophy while we're busy obtaining the principles. When the time comes to build our philosophical appreciation of the world, we should be sure that the data upon which we construct these more elaborate opinions were properly obtained.

Here we are then, ready to cross the Rubicon. I shall lead from the front; as soon as I am done writing, I'll set to the task of dismantling my own beliefs, favourites first, and building a new, independent world view. It will be painful at first, I know that, but I also anticipate the thrill of liberation. Like the rest of my species, I have been kept stooped under the yoke laid upon my shoulders by the illusion of knowledge. As shocking as it may be to admit, it is a self-inflicted burden, and I alone have the means to free myself.

While his followers desperately try to rescue black holes from ignominy by proposing mathematical escape clauses like "grey holes" and other such nonsense, Dr Hawking is immutable. He knows that without a horn on its forehead, a unicorn is just a horse.

Amen.

GLOSSARY

(In some cases, definitions are given both in plain English and in the language of physics).

Acceleration. A change in the rate (higher or lower) or direction of motion.

Adiabatic. A process without transfer of heat.

Analogue. Moving in a continuous, unbroken stream, as in information displayed on a dial.

Anisotropy. The manifestation of different characteristics when measured in opposing directions along an axis; uneven, asymmetrical distribution. (See: *isotropic*).

Antimatter. The inverse value of *matter*.

Atom. The smallest unit of matter; atoms are the fundamental components of a chemical reaction; a combination of protons, neutrons, and electrons.

Axiom. A statement assumed to be true to enable a chain of reasoning.

Baryonic matter. Matter composed of protons, neutrons, and electrons; the *standard model* for matter.

Belief. A conviction held without the need of proof.

Belief-synapse. A data-passing connection between articles of belief; an information bus that allows unrestricted flow between existing dogma and received belief. Belief-synapse allows the rapid creation or extension of a hypo-stack.

Big Bang. A hypothetical event, resembling a hybrid of an explosion and an implosion, postulated to mark the origin of the universe and the beginning of time; estimated to have occurred 13.7 billion +/- 800 thousand years ago.

Billion. One thousand million; 1,000,000,000; also expressed 10^9.

Binary. An expression using only two distinct elements. Binary notation is a system of numbers using only zeroes and ones.

Black body. An idealized, theoretical surface that absorbs and emits all radiation incidents upon it, and is therefore in thermal equilibrium. It has no capacity for reflection. Stars are assumed to be *blackbodies* for purposes of describing stellar radiation.

Black hole. Hypothetical concentration of mass, such that escape velocity exceeds the speed of light; controversial theoretical construct arising from arbitrary solutions to general relativity.

Bolometric. Involving radiant energy.

Brownian motion. The chaotic motion of molecules in a gas.

Canon. 1. In science, a principle or criterion in learning; 2. In philosophy, a standard of ethics or morality; 3. In religion, a church decree to constrain religious practice.

Celestial sphere. The imagined inverted dome upon which the characteristic stellar patterns appear.

Centre of gravity. A geometrical point in any material system at which the gravitational potential of the system is directed.

Chaos theory. A description of variations in the outcome of events that, although subject to deterministic laws, are nevertheless influenced by random ambient variables, e.g., the growth of a snowflake, weather forecasting.

Chromosome. A rod-like minute structure present in cell nuclei during division; contains *genes* and transmits hereditary characteristics.

Constant flux. A cosmological theory describing a continuous sequence of universal expansion and contraction.

Conservation of energy (matter). The axiom that the existence of something precludes the possibility of nothing.

Cosmic microwave background radiation (CMBR). The roughly isotropic short-wave radio noise enveloping the Earth, purported to be an image of the primordial cosmological fireball.

Cosmogony. The study of the evolution of the universe as a whole or of a component system within it

Cosmography. The universal equivalent of *geography*.

Cosmology. That part of astronomy that seeks to describe the origin and evolution of the universe; in its current incarnation, pseudo-scientific religionism.

Cosmos. The universe seen as a disciplined system.

Cosmological. The property or effect of the (nonlocal) *cosmos*.

Cosmological principle. The hypothesis, attributed to E. A. Milne, that the large-scale universe is homogeneous and isotropic.

Dark energy. An imagined repulsive force introduced to account for the acceleration of universal expansion.

Dark matter. An imagined attractive force introduced to account for perceived mass anomalies in astrophysical systems.

Digital. Divided into units. In mathematics, usually a sequence of numbers. Used here as a synonym for *quantised*.

Dogma. Philosophy held intransigently; unreasonable standpoint.

Doppler effect. A change in radiated wavelength due to relative motion.

Dualism. A theological term describing the separation of body and soul, and man and God.

Duality. Antithesis of *singularity*; the polarised form in which reality presents itself.

Energy. The capacity to do work and overcome resistance; the manifestation of that potential.

Entropy. Increased complexity.

Energy parity level. The point at which momentary balance between mass and kinetic energy is achieved; temporary tidal equilibrium.

Escape velocity. The minimum velocity that will allow an object to overcome gravity; approximately 40,000 km/h on Earth; the speed of light in a black hole.

Event. An interaction of energy that may be encapsulated by space-time coordinates.

Event horizon. The surface of an imaginary sphere marking the boundary of a black hole.

Event threshold. A point in space-time marking the commencing point of evolution, before and beneath which no further simplification can occur.

Evolution. The progressive, open-ended transformation of systems with time, usually selectively driven by function.

Faith drag (aka ideological inertia). A consequence of the power of belief over reason; the tendency of reason to trail belief; articles of faith that remain popularly in place despite the objective overturning of previously accepted supporting evidence; the time lag between a paradigm shift in science and a modification of belief to accommodate it.

Field. The spatial arrangement of energy potential.

Force. A condition with the potential to rearrange matter or change its rate of motion; a dynamic influence on acceleration.

Foreshortening (aka *Lorentz-Fitzgerald contraction*). A balancing factor introduced to special relativity to allow an absolutely constant speed of light.

Geocentric. Earth-centred (in cosmology).

Geodesic. Path of least resistance followed by matter in Einstein's curved space-time.

Gravity. The force of attraction between objects with mass; one of four fundamental forces of nature; considered in *relativity* theory to be an effect caused by curved space-time.

Hawking radiation. Particles (quanta of mass energy) that escape from a black hole.

Heat. The transfer of energy from a body with a higher temperature to a body with a lower temperature. (This is work at a molecular level without the presence of external forces.)

Hubble constant (H_0). The rate at which the universe is said to be expanding.

Hubble law. Proportionality seen between cosmic redshift and recessional motion in expanding universe theories.

Human consciousness unit (shell). The finite range of phenomena being investigated in this book

Hypo-stack. A contraction of *hypothesis* and *stack*; a model or part of a model constructed in interdependent layers of unresolved theoretical constructs; a philosophical house of cards.

Ideological inertia. A consequence of the power of belief over reason; the tendency of reason to trail belief; articles of faith that remain popularly in place despite the objective overturning of previously accepted supporting evidence; the time lag between a paradigm shift in science and a modification of belief to accommodate it. (See: faith drag)

Ideological momentum. The impetus of collective opinion; the tendency for supportive results to emerge from prior consensus or authority; also called "the snowball effect"; a synthetic trend in which we impute meaning in things just because we *want* meaning to be there for whatever deeply held reason, and then take that meaning forward even when it has been objectively falsified.

Infinity. A state of being limitless; unending.

Instinct. The innate capacity of an animal or human to respond to environmental conditions in a predetermined way; cellular will.

Intelligence. The ability to rationalise *and* appreciate aesthetics.

Investment bias. The influence on results stemming from the need to satisfy sponsors.

Isotropic. Having properties that do not vary with direction.

Kinetic energy. The energy of motion, e.g., momentum.

Light. Commonly, visible part of the range of electromagnetic radiation. Some light is invisible to humans.

Light year. The distance that light would travel in a vacuum in one year: 5 trillion 869 billion 713 million 600 thousand miles, or ~9.3 trillion kilometres.

Mass. The amount of matter an object contains, and therefore its resistance to force; a quantity of matter, defined by two properties: *inertia* and *gravity*.

Mass energy. The energy of attraction between systems, e.g., magnetism, gravity.

Matter. A form of energy that has substance, inertia, and coherence.

Million. One thousand times one thousand; 1,000,000; 10^6.

Model. Scientific: a mathematical approximation of a supposedly real situation.

Momentum. Inertia in motion.

Objective. 1. Not influenced by personal feelings or opinions. 2. Not dependent on the mind for existence; actual. (See: *subjective*)

Observer effect. Property of an observer that causes it to perceive an event subjectively.

Occam's Razor (aka Ockham's razor, owing to fourteenth-century English friar William of Ockham). In a hypothesis, making no superfluous argument; striving for the simplest effective solution.

Olbers' paradox. The question "why is the sky dark at night?" is usually taken rhetorically to imply a finite material universe. Other explanations are that light degrades with time and space to become invisible, or that we are shielded from background radiation by foreground material.

Perception. The ability of sentient beings to rationally translate sensory input to create a mental approximation of external reality.

Philosophy. An academic discipline concerned with the significance to mankind of natural phenomena.

Photon. The unit, or quantum, of electromagnetic energy (not just visible light).

Plenum. A satisfied vacuum. A saturation of outward pressure.

Polarity. Points in a system representing opposing characteristics; the force created by such points or poles.

Populant. Quantum of an astrophysical system, or the system itself.

Postulate. To suggest that something is true.

Propaganda. Arguments raised systematically with the intention of persuading people that a particular doctrine is true; information, especially of a biased or misleading nature, used to promote a political cause or point of view.

Quantum. A discrete quantity of energy, the smallest that can join or leave an energy system.

Quantum hypothesis. The suggestion by Max Planck that energy at atomic level is emitted and absorbed in discrete quantities.

Quantum jump (or **leap**). The movement of electrons between orbital shells in Niels Bohr's explanation of the quantum hypothesis; colloquially, a profound shift, for example, in opinion.

Quantum mechanics. A controversial theory of particle behaviour.

Radiation. The means by which energy transports itself.

Redshift. Redshift is a spectral signature commonly used in astrophysics, often invoked to indicate relative motion, and by implication, distance. A higher redshift object should be appreciably further away than one with lower redshift. Red and blue are colours at opposite ends of the light spectrum. Red light has a longer wavelength than blue, so a light source moving away from the observer would have its light waves stretched and thus spectral lines would be shifted towards the red end of the spectrum. That's redshift. The degree of shift or deflection in the lines is obtained by comparison to a benchmark taken to be the positions they occupy in local light, that is, sunlight. A source coming towards us would have its waves compressed, and spectral lines would be moved towards the blue (blueshift). Most celestial light sources are said to be moving away from the Earth, so the buzzword is redshift. The stretching or compression of a wave-form signal because of the relative motion of observer and the source of the signal is called the Doppler effect, and is readily appreciated in sound waves — when a motor car, for example, passes a stationary observer by the roadside, he hears the pitch of the sound drop as it moves away from him. That's the Doppler effect, and it causes redshift in light from a source that's receding from us.

Relativity. The role of frames of reference in measurement.

Religion. Cosmology that requires intervention of a supernatural, omnipotent personality in the management of the universe, and unquestioning faith in such an entity or entities.

Scale warping. A relativistic effect that distorts the results of measurements taken at great distances, macro or micro.

Schwarzschild radius. The radius of a sphere into which matter must be compressed in order to form a black hole. Represented by $2GM/c2$, where G is the gravitational constant, and M is the mass. The surface of a sphere with this radius would be the *event horizon* of a black hole, from which neither matter nor any form of radiation can escape. (See: *Hawking radiation*)

Singularity. The antithesis of *duality*. In astrophysics, a point in space-time where matter becomes infinitely compressed into a volume infinitesimally small; in philosophy, a place where God divides by zero; in common sense, *nothing*.

Space. An abstract, non-material, 3D volume that accommodates the universe and all events in it.

Spatial credibility factor. Uncertainty brought about by remoteness; the requirement for theoretical abstraction proportional to distance from point of observation.

Standard model of cosmology. Abbreviated SCM, known properly as the *lambda cold dark matter model* or LCDMM, and referred to colloquially as *Big Bang theory* or BBT.

Static. In cosmology, an adjective qualifying the cosmos such that it does not organically expand; a static universe is none of spreading out, becoming less dense, or growing larger.

Steady state. A set of cosmological theories attributed mainly to Fred Hoyle, which describe an infinitely self-sustaining, expanding universe.

Subjective. 1. Based on or influenced by personal feelings, tastes, or opinions. 2. dependent on the mind for existence; virtual. (See: *objective*)

System (energy system). An integrated arrangement of matter comprised of quanta in equilibrium (in *coherence*). Systems vary enormously in size and scope; the range is probably greater than atomic nuclei to galactic superclusters.

Teleology. A philosophical doctrine suggesting that complex existence implies purpose and design; the belief that things are better explained by purpose than by cause.

Time. The continuous linear sequence of events, flowing always from past to future.

universe. Everything that exists. Subset: universe — a finite portion of the universe artificially bounded to facilitate analysis.

X-stream. The fundamental instruction set for the interactions of baryonic phenomena; that which exists eternally beneath the event threshold.

Zeitgeist. Literally, the spirit of the times; the defining mood of a particular period of history.

Zero point. On any scale of measurement, a complete absence of that being measured.

Zero point field. The contention in quantum mechanics that at zero point (for example, of temperature or vacuum), there is still energy.

BIBLIOGRAPHY

Note: I must emphasise that my personal paradigm shift came about as a result of reading a single book, fortuitously placed at the head of my alphabetical list — Robert Ardrey's 1966 masterpiece, *The Territorial Imperative*. Upon reflection, it seems to me that everything I have written since comes down to little more than a drawn-out expression of my own understanding of Ardrey's thesis.

Ardrey, Robert. *The Territorial Imperative*. New York: Atheneum, 1966.

Arp, Halton. *Catalogue of Discordant Redshift Associations*. Montreal: Apeiron, 2003.

Arp, Halton. *Quasars, Redshifts, and Controversies*. Berkeley: Interstellar Media, 1987.

Arp, Halton. *Seeing Red: Red shifts, Cosmology, and Academic Science*. Montreal: Apeiron, 1998.

Baggott, Jim. *Farewell to Reality: How Modern Physics Has Betrayed the Search for Scientific Truth*. Pegasus, 2013.

Behe, Michael J. *Darwin's Black Box*. New York: The Free Press, 1996.

Bering, Jesse. *The Belief Instinct*. New York: W. W. Norton & Co., Inc., 2011.

Calder, Nigel. *Einstein's universe*. New York: Viking Press, 1979.

Clegg, Brian. *Infinity*. New York: Carroll & Graf Publishers, 2003.

Close, Frank. *Particle Physics: A Very Short Introduction*. Oxford: Oxford University Press, 2004.

Copernicus, Nicolaus. *On the Revolutions of the Heavenly Spheres*. New York: Prometheus Books, 1995.

Dawkins, Richard. *The God Delusion*. London: Transworld Publishers, 2006.

Derbyshire, John. *Prime Obsession*. Washington: Joseph Henry Press, 2003.

Einstein, Albert, and Leopold Infeld. *The Evolution of Physics*. New York: Simon and Schuster, 1938.

Einstein, Albert. *Letters to Solovine 1906–1955*. New York: Carol Publishing Group, 1993.

Einstein, Albert. *Out of my Later Years*. New York: Wings Books, 1996.

Einstein, Albert. *Relativity: The Special and the General Theory*. New York: Three Rivers Press, 1961.

Euclid. *The Thirteen Books of the Elements*. Translated by Sir Thomas Heath. New York: Dover Publications, 1956.

Faraday, Michael. *The Chemical History of a Candle*. New York: Crowell, 1957.

Ferris, Timothy. *The Whole Shebang*. New York: Touchstone, 1997.

Feynman, Richard P. *Surely You're Joking, Mr. Feynman!*. New York: W. W. Norton & Company, 1997.

Feynman, Richard P. *The Character of Physical Law*. New York: Modern Library, 1994.

Galilei, Galileo. *Dialogues Concerning Two New Sciences*. New York: Prometheus Books, 1991.

Gardner, Martin. *Did Adam and Eve Have Navels?* New York: W. W. Norton & Company, 2000.

Goldwag, Arthur. *Cults, Conspiracies, and Secret Societies*. Vintage Books, 2009.

Gould, Stephen Jay. *Full House*. New York: Harmony Books, 1996.

Greene, Brian. *The Elegant universe: Superstrings, Hidden Dimensions, and the Quest for the Ultimate Theory*. New York: Vintage Books, 2000.

Gribbin, John. *Stardust*. London: Penguin Books, 2001.

Harris, Sam. *Free Will New York*. Free Press, 2012.

Hawking, Stephen. *A Brief History of Time*. London: Bantam Press, 1988.

Hawking, Stephen. *The universe in a Nutshell*. London: Bantam Press, 2001.

Hawking, Stephen, and Leonard Mlodinow. *The Grand Design*. London: Bantam Press, 2010.

Herbert, Nick. *Quantum Reality*. New York: Anchor Books, New York 1985.

Hey, Tony, and Patrick Walters. *The New Quantum universe*. Cambridge: Cambridge University Press, 2003.

Hogan, James P. *Kicking the Sacred Cow*. New York: Baen Books, 2004.

Hoyle, Fred, and N. C. Wickramasinghe. *Lifecloud*. London: J. M. Dent & Sons Ltd., 1978.

Hoyle, Fred, Geoffrey Burbidge, and Jayant Narlikar. *A Different Approach to Cosmology*. Cambridge: Cambridge University Press, 2000.

Jammer, Max. *Concepts of Force*. Cambridge, MA: Harvard University Press, 1957.

Kepler, Johannes. *Epitome of Copernican Astronomy & Harmonies of the World*. New York: Prometheus Books, 1995.

Kuhn, Thomas. *The Structure of Scientific Revolutions*. Chicago: University of Chicago Press, 1966.

Laughlin, Robert B. *A Different universe (Reinventing Physics from the Bottom Down)*. New York: Basic Books, 2005.

Lerner, Eric J. *The Big Bang Never Happened*. New York: Vintage Books, 1992.

Lerner, Eric J., and José B. Almeida. (Editors) *Proceedings of the 1st Crisis in Cosmology Conference, CCC-I*. New York: AIP Conference Proceedings, vol. 822, 2006.

López Corredoira, Martín. *The Twilight of the Scientific Age*. Boca Raton, FL: Brown Walker Press, 2013.

Mach, Ernst. *Space and Geometry*. New York: Dover Pulications, 2004.

Marmet, Paul. *Absurdities in Modern Physics: A Solution*. Self-published,1993.

Maxwell, James Clerk. *Matter and Motion*. New York: Dover Publications, 1954.

Maxwell, James Clerk. *Treatise on Electricity and Magnetism*. New York: Dover Publications, 1954.

Mayr, Ernst. *What Evolution Is*. London: Phoenix, 2002.

Mitchell, William C. *Bye Bye Big Bang, Hello Reality*. Carson City: Cosmic Sense Books, 2002.

McTaggart, Lynne. *The Field*. London: Element, 2003.

Newton, Isaac. *The Principia: Mathematical Principles of Natural Philosophy.* Translated by I. Bernard Cohen and Anne Whitman. Berkeley: University of California Press, 1999.

Penrose, Roger. *The Emperor's New Mind.* Oxford: Oxford University Press, 1989.

Penrose, Roger. *The Road to Reality: A Complete Guide to the Laws of the universe.* London: Jonathan Cape, 2004.

Popper, Karl. *Logic of Scientific Discovery.* Abingdon: Routledge, 2002.

Ratcliffe, Hilton. *The Virtue of Heresy: Confessions of a Dissident Astronomer.* Milton Keynes: AuthorHouse, 2007.

Rolfs, Claus E., and William S. Rodney, *Cauldrons in the Cosmos.* Chicago: University of Chicago Press, 1988.

Sagan, Carl. *The Cosmic Connection.* London: Papermac, 1981.

Satel, Sally, and Scott O. Lilienfeld. *Brainwashed: The Seductive Appeal of Mindless Neuroscience.* Basic Books, 2013.

Sheldrake, Rupert. *Science Set Free.* New York: Deepak Chopra Books, 2012.

Shermer, Michael. *The Believing Brain.* New York: Times Books, 2011.

Smolin, Lee. *The Trouble with Physics: The Rise of String Theory, The Fall of a Science, and What Comes Next.* New York: Houghton Mifflin, 2006.

Unzicker, Alexander, and Sheilla Jones; *Bankrupting Physics: How Today's Top Scientists are Gambling Away Their Credibility.* Palgrave Macmillan, 2013.

Unzicker, Alexander, *The Higgs Fake: How Particle Physicists Fooled the Nobel Committee.* CreateSpace, 2013.

Weinberg, Steven. *Dreams of a Final Theory.* New York: Vintage Books, 1994.

Weinberg, Steven. *The First Three Minutes.* New York: Basic Books, 1977.

Whitehead, Alfred North, and Bertrand Russell. *Principia Mathematica.* Cambridge: Cambridge University Press, 1997.

Woit, Peter. *Not Even Wrong: The Failure of String Theory and the Search for Unity in Physical Law.* New York: Basic Books, 2006.

Zukav, Gary. *The Dancing Wu Li Masters.* New York: Harper Collins, 2001.

Zukav, Gary. *The Seat of the Soul.* London: Rider & Co., 1990.

ABOUT THE AUTHOR

HILTON RATCLIFFE IS A South African–born physicist, mathematician, and astronomer. He is a member of both the Astronomical Society of Southern Africa (ASSA) and the Astronomical Society of the Pacific (ASP). He became a founding member of the Alternative Cosmology Group (ACG) — an association of some seven hundred leading scientists from all corners of the globe), which conducted its inaugural international conference in Portugal in 2005.

He was an active member of the organisational, scientific, and proceedings committees for the second ACG conference, which was held in the United States in September 2008. Hilton has been frequently interviewed in the press, radio, and television, and has authored a number of papers for scientific journals, books, and conferences. For many years he wrote a monthly astrophysical column for *Ndaba*, newsletter of the ASSA's Durban Centre, and is editor of the *Monthly Notes of the Alternative Cosmology Group*. He serves as consulting astrophysicist on the steering committee of the Durban Space Science Centre and Planetarium, a project of ASSA's Durban Centre. Hilton Ratcliffe is best known in formal science as co-discoverer, together with eminent nuclear chemist Oliver Manuel and solar physicist Michael Mozina, of the CNO nuclear fusion cycle on the surface of the Sun, nearly seventy years after it was first predicted.

Besides this one, Hilton Ratcliffe has authored two books (*The Virtue of Heresy* and *The Static universe*) and contributed chapters to two others. In 2013, Ratcliffe's first book, *The Virtue of Heresy*, was nominated for the London School of Economics' prestigious Lakatos Award for literature judged to have been in exceptional service to science.

In his capacity as Fellow of the (British) Institute of Physics, he involves himself in addressing the decline in student interest in physical sciences at both high school and university level, and particularly likes to encourage the reading of books. Hilton Ratcliffe may be reached by email at *hilton@hiltonratcliffe.com*.